Volume 16: How to Detect and Handle Outliers

The ASQC Basic References in Quality Control: Statistical Techniques
Edward F. Mykytka, Ph.D., Editor

Volume 16: How to Detect and Handle Outliers

Boris Iglewicz and David C. Hoaglin

How to Detect and Handle Outliers
Boris Iglewicz and David C. Hoaglin

Library of Congress Cataloging-in-Publication Data

Iglewicz, Boris.
    How to detect and handle outliers / by Boris Iglewicz and David C.
Hoaglin.
        p.   cm. — (ASQC basic references in quality control; v. 16)
    Includes bibliographical references and index.
    ISBN 0-87389-247-X
    1. Outliers (Statistics)   I. Hoaglin, David C. (David Caster).
II. Title.   III. Series.
QA276.7.I35   1993
519.5—dc20   93-20842
                                                CIP

10 9 8 7 6 5 4 3 2 1

ISBN 0-87389-247-X

Acquisitions Editor: Susan Westergard
Production Editor: Annette Wall
Marketing Administrator: Mark Olson
Set in Computer Modern by Boris Iglewicz.
Cover design by Artistic License.
Printed and bound by BookCrafters, Inc.

ASQC Mission: To facilitate continuous improvement and increase customer satisfaction by identifying, communicating, and promoting the use of quality principles, concepts, and technologies; and thereby be recognized throughout the world as the leading authority on, and champion for, quality.

For a free copy of the ASQC Quality Press Publications Catalog, including ASQC membership information, call 800-248-1946.

Printed in the United States of America

 Printed on acid-free recycled paper

 ASQC
Quality Press
611 East Wisconsin Avenue
Milwaukee, Wisconsin 53202

The ASQC Basic References in Quality Control: Statistical Techniques is a continuing literature project of ASQC's Statistics Division. Its aim is to survey topics in statistical quality control in a practically usable, "how-to" form in order to provide the quality practitioner with specific, ready-to-use tools for conducting statistical analyses in support of the quality improvement process.

Suggestions regarding subject matter content and format of the booklets are welcome and will be considered for future editions and revisions. Such suggestions should be sent to the series editor(s).

Volumes Published

Contents

Acknowledgments

We wish to thank the editor of this series, Edward Mykytka, for his encouragement and valuable advice as we developed our manuscript. We are also grateful to the reviewers, whose suggestions led to a number of improvements. Moreover, we are indebted to Richard Heiberger for his timely assistance in transforming our LaTeX manuscript into the style of the "How To" series. In addition, we thank the following graduate students at Temple University: Quingxian Zhang for creating the figures and Wenjin Wang and Erin Hodgess for help with the simulations. David Hoaglin's work was facilitated in part by grant SES–8908841 from the National Science Foundation.

1

Abstract

Data sometimes include observations that don't appear to belong with the rest. If we understand in detail the mechanism that produces each observation, we might well be able to explain most of these anomalous results. For example, an instrument may have been calibrated improperly, a measurement may have been read incorrectly, an uncontrollable event may have affected the result, or a recording error may have crept in. Ordinarily we would act on such information by classifying the anomalous observations as outliers and setting them aside. Then our analysis would focus on the process that we intended to study.

In practice, we may have only partial information on mechanisms underlying the observations, and we may not know about unusual circumstances affecting some of the data. Thus we may have to rely primarily on the data in judging which observations are outliers. Historically, scientists, engineers, and statisticians have faced this challenge in a great variety of ways, responding to different needs and circumstances. A number of books cover the background and technical aspects and provide access to the extensive literature.

This booklet concentrates on the practical aspects of dealing with outliers in data that arise most often in applications: single and multiple samples, linear regression, and factorial experiments. For each setting we present a technique that works well (and perhaps some alternatives), explain the motivation for it, discuss its strengths and weaknesses, and illustrate its use in examples. Where special tables are required, we include them in the appendix.

Our intended audience includes practitioners in quality control, as well as workers in engineering and applied science who gather and analyze data. The booklet should also be helpful to advanced students in these fields and in statistics, both for a brief, practical introduction to the statistical treatment of outliers and as a stepping stone to more-comprehensive and more-technical treatments of the subject.

In the setting of a single sample we discuss three main approaches. First, *outlier labeling* aims to flag observations as possible outliers for further investigation. Second, when the main need is to calculate an estimate (for example, of an underlying mean or median), *outlier accommodation* empha-

1

sizes techniques that suffer little adverse effect when outliers are present, but that do not attempt to remove the outliers. Finally, techniques for *outlier identification* formally test whether observations are outliers so that they can be set aside. As a basis for making such tests at a specified significance level, we adopt the customary convention that the good observations can be adequately described as a sample from a normal distribution. Chapter 2 discusses some specific models that might generate outliers.

In Chapter 6 we go beyond the normal distribution to handle data that follow a lognormal distribution or an exponential distribution or that can be transformed to resemble a normal distribution.

In data that are being analyzed by regression, outliers pose a greater challenge because some observations can have disproportionate impact on the fitted regression. We discuss leverage and influence and some basic regression diagnostics in simple and multiple regression. We also present one simple technique, the repeated-median line, to illustrate the idea of regression methods that avoid the most severe adverse effects of outliers.

Balanced factorial experiments avoid some of these difficulties by giving each observation the same leverage. We explain this application of leverage and discuss the use of modified   charts for identifying outliers in replicated factorial experiments.

Selected references enable the reader to pursue each topic in greater depth. Furthermore, an index provides ready access to related material elsewhere in this booklet.

2

Introduction

Since the beginning of modern experimental science, many researchers have arbitrarily discarded observations that either seemed suspicious or deviated noticeably from a hypothesized model. Starting about 200 years ago, challenges to such a haphazard approach led to the introduction of more-formal statistical techniques for identifying observations that were candidates for elimination. Active research on appropriate methods for detecting outliers has continued to the present, and practitioners must now choose among a large number of techniques. One purpose of this booklet is to introduce and discuss a small subset of the available methods that are most suitable for application.

Quality control practitioners help gather and analyze a considerable amount of data, often of a repetitive nature. For example, control-chart limits are typically based on at least 20 rational subgroups. Outliers may then provide important information on the process or the quality of the data. Such outliers may indicate faulty data recording, confusion about the definition of key quality standards, or choice of the wrong statistical model. This booklet advocates the belief that it is sound policy to inspect all data for outliers. Exploratory searches then seek the causes for the outlying observations. In this context, the identification of outliers as faulty observations is only one part of the outlier-handling process.

Outlier-detection rules sometimes falsely identify observations as outliers. Conversely, certain popular outlier-detection rules are incapable of identifying gross outliers in some situations. Practical methods should balance these two types of errors. Since discarding any observations requires great care, any statistical rule used for that purpose must be formal and conservative. Far looser rules can serve when the purpose is to detect outliers and then investigate possible underlying causes. This booklet presents outlier-detection rules as exploratory devices, in the hope that users will not be too uncomfortable with the occasional identification of *false* outliers. An entire chapter discusses less formal outlier-labeling rules for use as exploratory tools.

One use of quality control data is to estimate population parameters. For example, it may be useful to estimate the average proportion of defectives or the average diameter of produced cylinders. Estimation methods developed in recent years can accommodate outliers. These robust/resistant estimators tolerate a moderate number of outlying observations without needing

2.1
Background

3

to detect possible outliers and consider rejecting them. Such methods have received little notice in the quality control literature. Thus this booklet includes an introduction to outlier-accommodation procedures and references to more detailed discussions.

2.2 Definition of Outlier

Although most professionals intuitively understand the meaning of *outlier*, careful scrutiny reveals varied interpretations. Barnett and Lewis (1984, p. 4), in a very thorough and quite readable book on outliers, state that an outlier is "an observation (or subset of observations) which appears to be inconsistent with the remainder of that set of data." A similar definition appears in Hawkins's slightly more mathematical and shorter book on outliers (1980, p. 1). He defines an outlier as "an observation which deviates so much from other observations as to arouse suspicions that it was generated by a different mechanism." Alternatively, Beckman and Cook (1983, p. 121), in a wide-ranging and valuable review paper on outliers, define an outlier as "a collective to refer to either a contaminant or a discordant observation." A *discordant observation* is "any observation that appears surprising or discrepant to the investigator." Similarly, a *contaminant* is "any observation that is not a realization from the target distribution."

An example may help clarify differences between these definitions. Consider the following hypothetical random sample.

| 7.42 | 7.36 | 7.81 | 7.63 | 7.57 | 7.48 | 7.39 | 17.64 | 7.56 | 7.41 |
| 7.76 | 7.53 | 7.87 | 7.41 | 7.62 | 7.51 | 7.47 | 7.92 | 7.39 | 7.54 |

The number 17.64 stands out, and most quality control professionals would consider it an outlier. The rest of the data seems to have come from a single source.

Suppose that further investigation of the data reveals a total of four measurement errors caused by an incorrect setting of the instrument. With the errors underlined the data are as follows:

| 7.42 | 7.36 | <u>7.81</u> | 7.63 | 7.57 | 7.48 | 7.39 | <u>17.64</u> | 7.56 | 7.41 |
| 7.76 | 7.53 | <u>7.87</u> | 7.41 | 7.62 | 7.51 | 7.47 | <u>7.92</u> | 7.39 | 7.54 |

Three of the four measurement errors resulted in values that do not immediately stand out in this list and thus were not considered outliers. For this reason, Barnett and Lewis (1984) and Hawkins (1980) would list 17.64 as the sole outlier in these data. According to Beckman and Cook (1983), on the other hand, the four measurement errors would be considered outliers, as they come from a different distribution. This booklet adopts the definition of Barnett and Lewis.

Care must be taken in distinguishing between discordant observations and outliers, as suspicious observations routinely occur in random samples. To illustrate this point, consider an observation whose value is 3, presumed to come from a standard normal distribution. At first glance such a value seems unlikely, as the probability that a single standard normal observation is 3 or greater equals $1 - \Phi(3) = .00135$. If, actually, the observation at 3 happens to be the largest of 40 random observations from a hypothesized standard normal distribution, then the probability that it is 3 or greater must be calculated from the distribution of the largest observation. This probability equals $1 - (1 - .00135)^{40} = .053$. In summary, an observation of 3 is considered an outlier in a sample of size one from a standard normal distribution, but not in a sample of size 40. The probability continues to grow as the sample size increases; for a sample of size 100, it is .126.

2.3 Outlier-Generating Models

Studies of how techniques behave when the data include outliers have often used mathematical models of chance mechanisms that produce such observations. The two most popular outlier-generating models are the slippage model and the mixture model. These outlier-generating models do not completely represent the true stochastic mechanisms that create outliers in practice, but they provide a controlled framework that is extremely useful in understanding the practical implications of outliers.

The *slippage model* has been the most popular mathematical model for both theoretical and empirical studies. This model assumes that the random sample of n observations consists of $n - r$ observations from $N(\mu, \sigma^2)$ (that is, a normal distribution with mean μ and standard deviation σ) and r observations from a different distribution. Thus, this model has the potential of generating up to r "true" outliers. The simplest choices for the alternative distribution involve a shift of location or a shift of scale.

Location-Shift Model: The r observations come from the $N(\mu + a, \sigma^2)$ distribution.

Scale-Shift Model: The r observations come from the $N(\mu, b\sigma^2)$ distribution.

Quality control professionals may recognize the location-shift model from ARL (average run length) studies of control charts.

An alternative approach for generating outliers uses a *mixture model*. Assume that the uncontaminated data come from a distribution G_1, and the contaminating data come from a distribution G_2. Then the n observations come from a mixture distribution

$$(1 - p)G_1 + pG_2,$$

where p is a fixed constant between 0 and 1. In this model the number of observations actually obtained from distribution G_2 is a random variable, because each of the n observations has probability p of coming from G_2 and probability $1 - p$ of coming from distribution G_1. There are no contaminants when $p = 0$, but the entire sample consists of contaminants when $p = 1$.

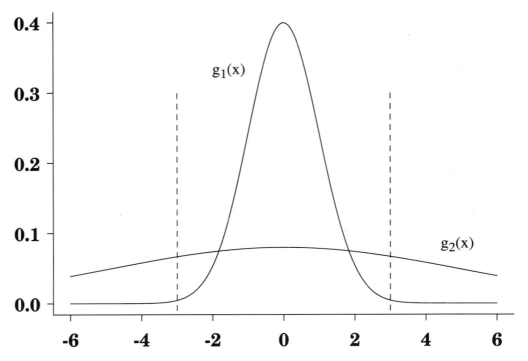

Figure 2.1. The two components of a scale-shift model. The uncontaminated data come from $G_1 = N(0, 1)$ with density g_1 and the contaminating data come from $G_2 = N(0, 25)$ with density g_2. If observations outside the lines at ± 3 are regarded as discordant, then only 55% of the observations from G_2 will be declared outliers.

Figure 2.1 sketches the scale-shift model with $\mu = 0$, $\sigma = 1$, and $b = 25$. Assume further that observations whose absolute value exceeds 3 will be considered discordant. Then an observation from $N(0, 25)$ will not always be an outlier. In fact, only about 55% of such observations will be declared outliers. Thus, popular outlier-generating models produce some outliers plus many observations that seem compatible with the uncontaminated distribution.

Both mathematical models and extensive experience point toward the need for routine inspection of data for outliers. Although outliers are occasionally isolated, unreliable observations, they often arise from an assignable cause. In such cases, the outliers are often the "tip of the iceberg." Discovery of the cause reveals many additional contaminated observations hidden within the bulk of the data. Of greater importance, knowledge of the cause contributes to a better understanding of the process and may aid the search for improvements. As a reviewer of the draft manuscript for this booklet pointed out, "Outliers are sometimes gems—containing the most valuable information from the investigation."

Outliers need not be contaminants. They may merely indicate that the wrong model or distribution has been assumed. Thus, assuming normality for lognormal data will typically lead to discordant observations that are identifiable as outliers.

2.4 Why Study Outliers?

We recommend that data be routinely inspected for outliers, because outliers can provide useful information about the data. At the same time, methods for identifying outliers need to be used carefully, as it is quite easy to confuse discordant random observations and outliers. Outlier investigations are useful because outliers have many potential causes; each cause provides an opportunity for improving the quality of the data-gathering process or for identifying practical alternative models that may prove more appropriate for making statistical inferences. Some possible sources for outliers are as follows:

- Outliers can arise from *gross recording or measurement errors*. Although a data set may have only one or two isolated outliers, the sample may contain many more defective observations that do not arouse suspicion. Thus, identifying the causes for such outliers, followed by appropriately removing them, can considerably reduce the rate of data errors in future samples. This is particularly important in quality control practice, where repetitive sample gathering is common.

- An *incorrect distributional assumption* may produce outliers. A common mistake is to assume that the data are normally distributed when, in fact, they come from a substantially different distribution. Such data may frequently contain observations that appear to be outliers. Use of the proper statistical model usually shows that these observations are not true outliers, but only unlikely observations from the normal distribution. In such situations, the resulting investigation for outliers can lead to a more suitable statistical model and, hence, to more appropriate statistical inferences.

- Outliers, on occasion, indicate that *the data contain more structure* than is being used. For example, presumed random daily samples may actually be composed of morning and afternoon subsamples, which need to be investigated in the proper paired framework.

- On occasion an *unusual observation* merely indicates that such a value is possible. A careful investigation of the conditions that led to this observation can result in an important and useful discovery. Such a discovery has the potential of greatly improving the process or leading to the production of superior or alternative products.

7

2.5 How to Handle Outliers

Routine inspection of data for outliers serves mainly to identify their causes and then to make this information available to future studies. We still face the question of what to do with the identified outliers. This question actually deals with two actions: (1) how to record the data, and (2) what use to make of the identified outliers in the ensuing data analysis. We discuss these required actions separately.

Recording of identified outliers. We strongly recommend that outliers be carefully recorded as part of the collected data, with descriptions of any identified causes placed next to the values. Recording of the outliers is encouraged even when their causes are easily explained errors, such as incorrect data recording or coding. Because such errors are frequently repetitive, persistent recording serves as an effective reminder to take appropriate action to remove the problem. On the other hand, not recording such values may result in reduced attention to potentially serious problem areas. In summary, all outliers should be recorded, as a noticeable proportion of outliers can provide sufficient information to take action to improve the data-gathering process or to decide that an alternative distributional model is more appropriate.

Outliers need not represent defective observations, but they can indicate the need for an alternative model or provide potentially useful information about the process. Such outliers need not occur frequently. The best way to ensure that the resulting information is not lost is to record each outlier and then attempt to discover the assignable causes.

The role of the outliers in data analysis. Analysts should be concerned about using observations that have been identified as unreliable because of faulty recording or poorly calibrated or defective measuring instruments. An effective way out of this dilemma is to use robust statistics, which will be minimally affected by the outliers. Then the analyst can use all the observations. We encourage increased use of robust statistics, and we provide a more detailed discussion of such measures in Chapters 3 and 4.

For reasons such as continuity of procedure and limitations of software, many quality control practitioners may still use the traditional nonrobust statistical measures such as the sample mean. Such measures can be seriously affected by outliers. For this reason, care must be taken as to which observations to include. Outliers whose causes have not been clearly determined should be used in the data analysis, even when they appear to be in error. At the same time, clearly identified errors should either be corrected or not used in a traditional data analysis, as these can have a misleading influence on the conclusions. This approach leaves situations where the outliers do not quite represent gross errors, but their causes are only partially identified. Such borderline cases require sound judgment and a realistic assessment of the practical implications of retaining the outliers. Often it is possible to make at least an informal assessment of the impact of the outliers by carrying out two analyses: one that retains the presumed outliers and another that excludes them.

8

3

Outlier Labeling

A prudent data analyst often visually inspects data before performing a planned statistical analysis. Such a preliminary examination sometimes reveals suspicious observations, which further investigation may show to be outliers. Although skilled investigators can spot improbable values, they can easily miss or mislabel other types of outliers.

A preliminary determination of the location and number of outliers can prove helpful in deciding which outlier-detection test to use. Because some of the more powerful outlier-identification procedures depend heavily on such information, a poor preliminary judgment can lead to erroneous test results. For this reason, approximate information on the number and location of outliers can help in formally identifying them.

It is often difficult to detect outliers through visual inspection without the aid of analytic or graphical tools. In a revealing and educational experiment, Collett and Lewis (1976) measured the ability of college students to detect a true outlier in a sample consisting of nine random normal observations plus an outlier that was placed as the largest observation. Collett and Lewis presented the data as either an unordered list, an ordered list, or a graphical display. Additionally, they used several choices for the sample variance of the nine random observations. The experimenters aimed to learn whether these factors played an important role in a student's ability to detect the true outlier. The results showed that ordering the data greatly enhanced the chances of correctly identifying the largest observation as an outlier. Also, greater variability made it *more* likely that the largest value was considered an outlier. Collett and Lewis felt that the latter result occurred because respondents based their decisions on the difference between the two largest observations rather than on the overall scale of the data.

The experiment of Collett and Lewis indicates that visual inspection alone is not a reliable way to identify potential outliers. A superior approach uses a specific function of the observations. Such a measure aims not to identify observations as definite outliers, but only to label them as sufficiently suspect to merit further investigation. In short, an outlier-labeling rule is an improved alternative to visual inspection.

This chapter uses the following simple hypothetical data set to illustrate key concepts.

3.1 Reasons for Outlier Labeling

$$2.1 \quad 2.6 \quad 2.4 \quad 2.5 \quad 2.3 \quad 2.1 \quad 2.3 \quad 2.6 \quad 8.2 \quad 8.3$$

Of these 10 numbers, two are clear outliers. These two outliers may be data errors, or the data may have come from a mixture of two distributions. Other data sets may not be as clear-cut, enhancing the need for an appropriate data-labeling rule.

3.2   Z-Scores

Z-scores are sometimes used to screen data for outliers. The Z-scores are based on the well-known property of the normal distribution that if X is distributed as $N(\mu, \sigma^2)$, then $Z = (X - \mu)/\sigma$ is distributed as $N(0, 1)$. Consequently it is tempting to use the Z-scores of the observations $x_1, x_2, \cdots, x_n$,

$$z_i = (x_i - \bar{x})/s, \text{ where } s = \sqrt{\frac{\sum_{i=1}^{n}(x_i - \bar{x})^2}{n-1}},$$

as a method for labeling outliers. One popular rule labels Z-scores that exceed 3 in absolute value as outliers. This approach has an attractive simplicity, and most statistical software packages and even simple calculators make it easy to obtain the Z-scores. For the hypothetical data set given above, however, the Z-scores are

$$-.58 \quad -.38 \quad -.46 \quad -.42 \quad -.50 \quad -.58 \quad -.50 \quad -.38 \quad 1.87 \quad 1.91$$

Surprisingly, none exceeds 3. What went wrong? The answer lies in the constraint on each z_i that we have introduced through subtracting $\bar{x}$ from x_i and, especially, dividing $x_i - \bar{x}$ by s. A large value of $|x_i - \bar{x}|$ contributes to s and thus keeps the corresponding z_i from becoming arbitrarily large. Specifically, Shiffler (1988) showed that the absolute value of a Z-score is at most $(n-1)/\sqrt{n}$.

For selected values of n, the maximum possible Z-score, which we denote by $Z_{\max}$, is as follows:

n	$Z_{\max}$
5	1.79
10	2.85
11	3.02
15	3.61
20	4.25

Thus, for a sample size as small as $n = 10$, the seemingly reasonable criterion of labeling x_i as an outlier if $|z_i| > 3$ is doomed to failure because $|z_i| \leq Z_{\max} = 2.85$. It is not appropriate to think of a Z_i as being approximately normally distributed. We conclude that Z-scores are *not* satisfactory for outlier labeling, especially in small data sets.

Although the basic idea of using Z-scores is a good one, they are unsatisfactory because the summaries $\bar{x}$ and s are not resistant. A *resistant* summary or estimator is not unduly affected by a few unusual observations. Clearly, $\bar{x}$ and s can be greatly affected by even one single outlier. To illustrate this shortcoming, assume that $n-1$ observations have similar values and one observation differs greatly from the rest. Such samples arise as worst cases in discussions of how estimators respond to outliers. This situation can be approximated by taking

$$x_1 = x_2 = \cdots = x_{n-1} = x \text{ and } x_n = x + ny.$$

Then $\bar{x} = x + y$, and for $y > 0$, $s = y\sqrt{n}$. Thus, $\bar{x}$ and s go to infinity as y goes to infinity. As a consequence, the largest Z-score, for this case, is given by

$$Z_n = \frac{x + ny - (x + y)}{y\sqrt{n}} = (n-1)/\sqrt{n}.$$

This is the same result as the maximum possible Z-score, $Z_{\max}$. $Z_{\max}$ does not depend on the data values, but only on the number of observations.

Our alternative to Z-scores uses resistant estimators. To be successful, the estimators should not be unduly affected by changes in a fair proportion of the sample. Such estimators are said to have a high *breakdown point*. Some sources use the term *breakdown bound* instead of *breakdown point* for the same concept. The *breakdown point* of an estimator is defined as the largest proportion of the data that can be replaced by arbitrary values without causing the estimated value to become infinite. Thus, the sample mean, standard deviation, and range have breakdown points of zero, as one observation moved to infinity would make these estimators infinite. The sample median, on the other hand, has a breakdown point of approximately 50% (the exact percentage depends on whether the sample size is even or odd). The actual breakdown point of the median for n odd is $100((n-1)/2)/n\% = 50(1 - 1/n)\%$, and the corresponding percentage for n even is $100((n-2)/2)/n = 50(1 - 2/n)$. Because of its high breakdown point, we replace $\bar{x}$ by the sample median, which we denote by $\tilde{x}$.

We need a suitable replacement for s as well. For this purpose we use the estimator MAD (the median of the absolute deviations about the median).

$$MAD = \text{median}_i\{|x_i - \tilde{x}|\}$$

This estimator also has an approximately 50% breakdown point and is relatively easy to compute. The median and MAD now yield modified Z-scores, defined as follows:

$$M_i = \frac{0.6745(x_i - \tilde{x})}{MAD}$$

11

Table 3.1

Computation of modified Z-scores for the hypothetical data set ($\tilde{x} = 2.45$).

i	Data, x_i	Ordered x_i	Ordered $|x_i - \tilde{x}|$	M_i
1	2.1	2.1	.05	−1.57
2	2.6	2.1	.05	.67
3	2.4	2.3	.15	−.22
4	2.5	2.3	.15	.22
5	2.3	2.4	.15	−.67
6	2.1	2.5	.15	−1.57
7	2.3	2.6	.35	−.67
8	2.6	2.6	.35	.67
9	8.2	8.2	5.75	25.86
10	8.3	8.3	5.85	26.31

The constant 0.6745 is needed because $\text{E}(MAD) = 0.6745\sigma$ for large n.

Observations will be labeled outliers when $|M_i| > D$. We suggest using $D = 3.5$, relying on the following table from a simulation study, whose entries are the values of D that cause the stated proportion of random normal observations to be labeled as outliers. These results are based on 10,000 replications of n pseudo-normal observations for each sample size.

n	10%	5%	2.5%
10	3.41	4.19	5.08
20	3.26	3.78	4.25
40	3.22	3.60	3.92

These simulation results confirm that the outlier-labeling rule based on modified Z-scores can serve as a guide for labeling outliers.

We now use the hypothetical data set to illustrate the computation of the M_i scores. In Table 3.1 the second column lists the observations, and the third column contains the ordered values. To compute the median, we count in $(n+1)/2 = (10+1)/2 = 5.5$ observations in the ordered data; that is, we average the fifth and sixth ordered values. Thus $\tilde{x} = (2.4 + 2.5)/2 = 2.45$. The fourth column of Table 3.1 contains the ordered $|x_i - \tilde{x}|$. The MAD is their median. Thus $MAD = (0.15 + 0.15)/2 = 0.15$. The M_i scores can now be easily computed as $0.6745(x_i - 2.45)/0.15$. These entries appear in the fifth column of Table 3.1. The M_i entries corresponding to the values 8.2 and 8.3 are 25.86 and 26.31, respectively. This simple numerical example illustrates that, unlike Z-scores, the M_i values are capable of identifying obvious outliers.

Next, consider a second numerical example, in which the outliers may be more difficult to detect. The computations are similar to those from the previous example and, therefore, are not shown here. This time the hypothetical data set is as follows:

$$1.03 \quad 0.96 \quad 1.11 \quad 0.76 \quad 1.02 \quad 0.98 \quad 0.89 \quad 2.34 \quad 1.01 \quad 1.00$$

For this data set, 2.34 clearly appears to be an outlier. Some investigators may also find 0.76 suspicious. The M_i scores can help in determining the number of potential outliers. The M_i scores for this data set are

$$0.48 \quad -0.87 \quad 2.02 \quad -4.72 \quad 0.29 \quad -0.48 \quad -2.22 \quad 25.73 \quad 0.10 \quad -0.10$$

It is now convincing that this data set actually contains two outliers: 0.76 and 2.34.

In summary, the M_i scores can be used effectively to label outliers. The identified values can be studied further to explore possible explanations for these discordancies. These scores can also prove helpful in deciding on an appropriate formal statistical outlier-identification test to use.

3.4 Boxplots

A superior outlier-labeling rule forms a part of the popular graphical display called the boxplot. The boxplot is available, in various versions, on many major statistical software packages. For a more thorough discussion of alternative boxplot choices see Frigge, Hoaglin, and Iglewicz (1989). The boxplot version found in Tukey (1977) will be used throughout this booklet.

The main ingredients for a boxplot are the median, the lower quartile (Q_1), and the upper quartile (Q_3). In a large sample or a large population, one quarter of the values lie below Q_1, and three quarters lie below Q_3 (hence one quarter lie above Q_3). In a small or moderate sample, however, "one quarter" is usually only approximate. Later in this section we adopt one specific definition of the sample quartiles. For now, we need only the general idea.

Figure 3.1 shows a typical boxplot. The box contains a central line, usually at the median, and extends from Q_1 to Q_3. Cutoff points, known as *fences*, lie $1.5(Q_3 - Q_1)$ above the upper quartile and below the lower quartile. The outermost observations inside these fences become the endpoints of dashed lines extending out from the box. Observations beyond the fences are plotted separately and labeled as *outside values*. Using a liberal approach, we refer to the outside values as outliers.

Tukey (1977) uses the median for the central line and then defines the lower *fourth* (one type of quartile) as $Q_1 = x_{(f)}$, the fth ordered observation. Here f is computed as

$$f = \frac{\lfloor (n+1)/2 \rfloor + 1}{2},$$

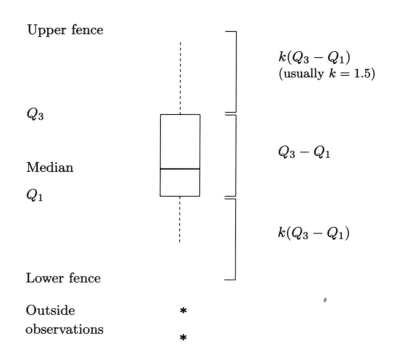

Figure 3.1. A typical boxplot showing the definitions of its ingredients. Two outside observations, plotted as *, lie below the lower fence.

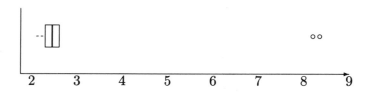

Figure 3.2. Boxplot for the data of Table 3.1. No data values lie between the upper fourth and upper fence. The observations at 8.2 and 8.3 are labeled as far out.

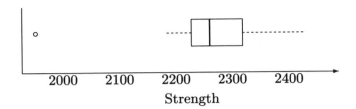

Figure 3.3. Boxplot for the gear-teeth data. One observation (plotted as 0) seems clearly smaller than the rest.

---

where $\lfloor x \rfloor$ represents the greatest integer $\leq x$. If f involves a fraction, Q_1 is the average of $x_{(\lfloor f \rfloor)}$ and $x_{(\lfloor f+1 \rfloor)}$. Hoaglin (1983) discusses the background for this definition. To get the upper quartile, Q_3, one similarly counts f observations from the top. That is, $Q_3 = x_{(n+1-f)}$. The *interquartile range*, also known as the *F-spread*, is now computed as $R_F = Q_3 - Q_1$.

Some boxplots and outlier-labeling schemes use cutoff points other than the fences. These cutoffs take the form $Q_1 - kR_F$ and $Q_3 + kR_F$. Tukey's boxplot, for example, uses $k = 3.0$ in addition to $k = 1.5$, with values outside the $k = 3$ limits declared *far out*, to distinguish them from *outside* observations, which lie outside the $k = 1.5$ limits but not beyond the $k = 3$ limits. We label outside values with asterisks and far out values with "0".

As an illustrative example, we construct a boxplot for the first hypothetical data set, shown in order in the third column of Table 3.1. For $n = 10$, we get $f = (\lfloor (10+1)/2 \rfloor + 1)/2 = (5+1)/2 = 3$. Thus, $Q_1 = 2.3$, $Q_3 = 2.6$, and $R_F = 0.3$. Then $1.5R_F = 0.45$, and $3R_F = 0.9$. The fences fall at $Q_1 - 1.5R_F = 1.85$ and $Q_3 + 1.5R_F = 3.05$, so a dashed line extends down from the box to 2.1, and the upper dashed line is absent. Indeed, with $Q_3 + 3R_F = 3.5$ we label 8.2 and 8.3 as far out observations. Finally, the median equals 2.45. These ingredients yield the boxplot in Figure 3.2.

For these data the boxplot was able to label the two largest observations as outliers, in addition to graphically summarizing the basic features of location, spread, and skewness. Thus, the boxplot labels outliers as part of the data summary, prodding the experimenter to routinely investigate and try to explain observations labeled as outliers.

As a second numerical example, consider the gear-teeth strength measurements on teeth 6 and 8 as given by Gunter (1988).

2431 2250 2311 2210 2329 2263 2353 2251 2275 2185 1958

The boxplot for this data set appears in Figure 3.3. This boxplot labels only the observation 1958 as far out. Therefore, this data set contains one potential outlier.

Table 3.2

The probability (in percentages) that the boxplot rule labels one or more observations outside in a sample of n observations from the standard normal distribution.

n	$k = 1.0$	$k = 1.5$	$k = 2.0$	$k = 3.0$
10	42.4	19.8	9.4	2.6
20	57.7	23.2	8.2	1.1
30	70.5	28.4	9.4	0.8
50	83.7	36.5	9.4	0.4
100	96.7	52.3	11.5	0.3

Source: Frigge, M., D. C. Hoaglin, and B. Iglewicz. 1989. "Some Implementations of the Boxplot." *The American Statistician* 43: 50–54. Entries from Table 1 on p. 53. Reprinted by permission of the American Statistical Association.

Hoaglin, Iglewicz, and Tukey (1986) reported an extensive study of the probability properties of the boxplot labeling rule. Table 3.2 partially summarizes their results. This table lists values of the probability of labeling at least one observation as an outlier in a random normal sample. We denote this probability by $D(k, n)$, because it depends on k and n. For $k = 1$, found in some computer packages, this probability is quite high (e.g., .577 for $n = 20$). The entries in the column for $k = 1.5$ indicate clearly why the boxplot rule is considered an outlier-labeling rule rather than an identification rule. From $D(1.5, 20) = .232$, we see that approximately one in four random normal samples will contain observations labeled as outside. The $k = 3.0$ rule is quite conservative, implying that far out values can be comfortably declared as outliers when the data are assumed to come from random normal samples. For more formal outlier testing, Hoaglin and Iglewicz (1987) obtained values of k that solve $D(k, n) = .10$ and also $D(k, n) = .05$. Although these values vary with n, they approximately equal 2.0 for $D(k, n) = .10$ and 2.2 for $D(k, n) = .05$.

Because about one in four boxplots of normal data contains at least one false outlier, the boxplot outlier-labeling rule provides only an exploratory tool. Observations flagged as outside require further study to determine their causes. This rule should not be used alone to declare outside observations as defective. The $k = 3$ rule, on the other hand, ordinarily does provide a conservative test for outliers.

Although the boxplot rule is not the most efficient way to label outliers, it has valuable features. The most important aspect of this rule is that it routinely labels outliers as part of a standard univariate data summary. As a consequence, the investigator gets an early warning to deal with the outside values and attempt to explain why they occurred. The boxplot makes the study of outliers more important than an isolated task to be performed when suspected observations are noted; it is a routine procedure to be performed on each data set.

Outlier Accommodation

Data are often used in estimation. Outliers can bias estimates and, as a consequence, may produce misleading results. This danger is greatest for the mean and other classical estimators that provide no protection against the presence of a few recording errors or measurements obtained from poorly calibrated instruments.

Research in statistics has produced a number of alternative estimators that are resistant and thus accommodate outliers. Such estimators are minimally affected by a moderate proportion of discordant observations. As a consequence, even grossly discordant observations do not unduly distort estimates. Our aim is to briefly introduce the concept of outlier accommodation, suggest several practical alternative estimators, and indicate the advantages of using such estimators in practice. In particular, the reader should consider using a trimmed mean when conditions warrant. For readers who wish further information, Chapters 9 through 12 of Hoaglin, Mosteller, and Tukey (1983) discuss estimators of location and scale at a relatively nontechnical level.

To illustrate these concepts, consider again the 11 observations on strength of gear teeth.

2431 2250 2311 2210 2329 2263 2353 2251 2275 2185 1958

Assume that we are interested in estimating the population average strength from these teeth. The most common estimator for this purpose is the sample mean $\bar{X}$. The estimate for the population mean would then be $\bar{x} = 2256.0$.

The boxplot in Figure 3.3, however, has already flagged 1958 as "far out," and the mean would give it full weight. Thus, we may face a difficult choice in deciding whether to use this observation when computing the sample mean. If we decide that 1958 is sufficiently suspect, we may wish to guard against it (and any other unusually low observation) by dropping the smallest observation in the sample before calculating the mean. To preserve symmetry and avoid bias, we also remove the largest value, in this instance 2431. The resulting trimmed mean, using the middle nine observations, is

$$\bar{x}_T = (2185+2210+2250+2251+2263+2275+2311+2329+2353)/9 = 2269.7.$$

As expected, $\bar{x}_T$ differs noticeably from $\bar{x}$. Although we would not regard the difference of about 14 units between $\bar{x}_T$ and $\bar{x}$ as dramatic, $\bar{x}_T$ does seem to fit in slightly better with the data (as shown, for example, in Figure 3.3). Ultimately we would hope to judge the effectiveness of a trimmed mean in this application on the basis of substantial further data on the strength of similar gear teeth. Many practitioners would consider $\bar{x}_T$ more reliable because the outlying observation 1958 does not affect it. In summary, trimming the largest observation and the smallest observation and averaging the remaining ones benefit this sample. Thus, we propose to use a trimmed mean instead of the sample mean in many situations.

In general, trimming takes out insurance against outliers by routinely dropping a fixed percentage of the data (or a fixed number of observations) at each end of the ordered sample. In this way we accommodate the outliers. Instead of labeling them and then deciding whether to use them, we leave them in the sample but do not include them in calculating the mean. The distinction is that trimming does not ask whether the observations being dropped are outliers. Indeed, they are usually good observations. By using fewer good observations, we expect the trimmed mean to be more variable, and hence less efficient. We may think of this loss of efficiency as an insurance premium that we pay to guard against the damage caused by the occasional outlier. In fact, the premium is often quite modest.

4.1 Trimmed Means

We now define the trimmed mean in terms of the ordered observations $X_{(1)}, X_{(2)}, \cdots, X_{(n)}$. The $100\alpha\%$ *trimmed mean*, $T(\alpha)$, is given by

$$T(\alpha) = \frac{1}{n(1 - 2\alpha)} \left[k(X_{(r+1)} + X_{(n-r)}) + \sum_{i=r+2}^{n-r-1} X_{(i)} \right],$$

where $r = \lfloor \alpha n \rfloor$, and $k = 1 - (\alpha n - r)$.

This formula is somewhat cumbersome when αn is not an integer (that is, when $k \neq 1$). This problem can be avoided by deliberately choosing a value of α that makes $k = 1$. Our suggestion is to use an approximately 15% trimmed mean, computed as follows:

1. Compute $d = 0.15(n + 1) = g + h$, where g is an integer and h is either a fraction or zero ($0 \leq h < 1$). Note that d has the same form as $0.5(n + 1)$, which is the depth of the sample median.

2. Let $r = g$ if $h < 0.5$; otherwise let $r = g + 1$.

3. Order the observations: $X_{(1)} \leq X_{(2)} \leq \cdots \leq X_{(n)}$.

4. Compute the trimmed mean T as

$$T = \frac{\sum_{i=r+1}^{n-r} X_{(i)}}{n - 2r}.$$

The estimator T is actually a $100(r/n)\%$ trimmed mean. Additionally, the breakdown point of T is $100(r/n)$, because up to r observations can be moved to infinity while still keeping T finite.

We now use the gear-teeth data to illustrate the computation of the trimmed mean. This data set consists of 11 observations. The steps required for computing T follow.

1. $d = 0.15(12) = 1.80$

2. Rounding yields $r = 2$

3. The ordered observations are as follows:

    1958 2185 2210 2250 2251 2263 2275 2311 2329 2353 2431

4.
$$\begin{aligned} T &= (2210 + 2250 + 2251 + 2263 + 2275 + 2311 + 2329)/7 \\ &= 2269.9 \end{aligned}$$

Previously we trimmed one observation at each end of the sample and got a trimmed mean of 2269.7. Now heavier trimming has produced nearly the same result. For this sample, minimal trimming avoids the distortion from one low observation. In general, we prefer to trim roughly 15% at each end for better protection.

4.2 Efficiency of Trimmed Means

The example shows that trimmed means are relatively easy to compute, and they also accommodate outliers. At the same time, the sample mean is the most efficient estimator of the population mean for random samples from the normal distribution. This property is an important argument for using $\bar{X}$. In order to justify the use of trimmed means, then, we must show that such estimators are also efficient for estimating the population mean. In fact, unlike the sample mean, trimmed means are quite efficient under a variety of distributional assumptions.

We now formally define the efficiency of the trimmed mean relative to the sample mean for estimating the population mean. Because these estimators are unbiased for symmetric distributions, we can compare their variances. Notice that if the distribution is not symmetric, then a symmetrically trimmed mean need not be unbiased. The *efficiency* E of the $100\alpha\%$ trimmed mean $T(\alpha)$, relative to the sample mean $\bar{X}$, is defined (in percentage terms) as

$$E = 100\text{Var}(\bar{X})/\text{Var}(T(\alpha)).$$

The relative efficiency E depends on the trimming fraction α, on the sample size n, and also on the distribution from which the data are assumed to come.

Table 4.1

Efficiency of median and recommended version of the 15% trimmed mean T relative to the mean for three distributions. The one-out distribution takes $n - 1$ observations from $N(0, 1)$ and one from $N(0, 16)$.

| | Normal | | Double-Exp. | | One-Out | |
n	Median	T	Median	T	Median	T
5	70	88	114	124	199	236
10	72	88	138	137	154	182
20	68	87	150	131	110	137

Source: Iglewicz, B., and D. C. Hoaglin. 1987. "Use of Boxplots for Process Evaluation." *Journal of Quality Technology* 19: 180–190. Entries from Table 3 on p. 188. Reprinted by permission of the *Journal of Quality Technology*.

To illustrate the roles of the trimming fraction, the sample size, and the underlying distribution, Table 4.1 shows the efficiency of two trimmed means for selected sample sizes ($n = 5, 10, 20$) from the normal distribution and two other symmetric distributions with heavier tails. One of the trimmed means is the median, which uses close to 50% trimming (40%, 40%, and 45% at the sample sizes listed). The other is the recommended 15% trimmed mean. The two heavier-tailed distributions are the double-exponential and the one-out, which takes $n - 1$ random observations from the standard normal and one observation from $N(0, 16)$. The one-out model produces samples with at most one outlier.

An inspection of the entries in Table 4.1 shows that the median is generally less efficient than the 15% trimmed mean. Thus, even though the median has a breakdown point of approximately 50%, estimators with less trimming have higher efficiency for these distributions and sample sizes. For normally distributed data in small samples, the 15% trimmed mean is approximately 90% as efficient as the mean. The slight advantage of the mean vanishes for the heavier-tailed distributions. The 15% trimmed mean is approximately 30% more efficient than the mean when the data come from a double-exponential distribution. Even more dramatic results emerge for the one-out distribution in small samples, where the 15% trimmed mean is almost twice as efficient as the mean. In summary, the mean is slightly more efficient for normally distributed data, but far less efficient in the presence of outliers.

Other studies have led to similar conclusions. In particular, the extensive robustness study by Andrews et al. (1972) has shown that 15% trimming yields at least 91% efficiency for normal data and quite high efficiency for data coming from distributions that generate some outliers. Thus, $T(15\%)$

is a fine estimator for normally distributed data and is not unduly affected by a small proportion of outliers.

Measures of variability are nearly as important as measures of location. In quality control the most familiar measures of variability are the range $R = X_{(n)} - X_{(1)}$ and the sample standard deviation

4.3 Scale Estimators

$$S = \sqrt{\frac{\sum_{i=1}^{n}(X_i - \bar{X})^2}{n-1}}.$$

As these two estimators illustrate, a discussion of measuring variability must often start by explaining what is to be measured. One basic difference between R and S is that they aim at different characteristics of the distribution from which the sample is assumed to come. For example, if the data are normal with population mean μ and population standard deviation σ, then the average value of S equals $c_4\sigma$, and $c_4 \to 1$ as $n \to \infty$; but R estimates another multiple of σ, namely $d_2\sigma$, which varies in a different way with the sample size. Thus S and R measure different characteristics of the normal distribution. Each yields an unbiased estimator of σ when we divide by the known constant; that is, S/c_4 and R/d_2 both estimate σ.

When we are estimating location under the usual assumption that the distribution is symmetric (but not necessarily normal), we do not face such a complication. The natural feature to aim at is the center of symmetry, and many measures of location (such as the trimmed means) give unbiased estimates.

Measurement of variability has no such natural target. If we thought that the data might come from some non-normal distribution, we could still use S and R to measure their variability, but we would have to change the value of c_4 and d_2 when we estimate σ for that distribution. We escape this constraint when we use a single measure to compare the variability of two or more samples that have the same size, but this is often a severe restriction. Thus, estimation is usually tied to a particular distribution. More technically, we have in mind a particular "location-scale family" of distributions, in which the "standard" probability density function is f_0, and we get the general density function f by specifying the location parameter θ and the scale parameter σ.

$$f(x) = \frac{1}{\sigma}f_0\left(\frac{x-\theta}{\sigma}\right)$$

Analogous to the way in which R and S relate differently to σ, we may redefine the scale parameter to be $\tau = k\sigma$ instead of σ. We have only to change f_0 by incorporating $1/k$ in the proper places. This arbitrariness of the scale parameter complicates our discussion of scale estimators, but it is an inherent feature of the situation. When we compare the robustness of scale estimators, we must allow for differences in scaling from one family of distributions to another. Fortunately, this is a manageable problem, and we turn to it later, when the need arises.

Neither R nor S is resistant, because they do not accommodate outliers. To provide resistance, the estimator known as MAD (Section 3.3) takes the median of the absolute deviations about the sample median $\tilde{X}$.

$$MAD = \text{median}_i\{|X_i - \tilde{X}|\}$$

This estimator of scale has a breakdown point of approximately 50%; thus, it accommodates outliers well. Another resistant estimator of scale, the *F-spread*, $R_F = X_{(n+1-f)} - X_{(f)}$, is discussed in Section 3.4.

A number of other approaches have produced estimators of scale, and Iglewicz (1983) discusses some of them. One of these approaches uses an approximate formula for the variance of an *M*-estimator of location in large samples. (In the discussion that follows we do not assume that the reader is familiar with *M*-estimators of location. Roughly, one can think of them as weighted means of the sample with weights that depend on the data and may require iterative calculations.) Even in moderate-sized samples the formula gives an estimator of scale that has high efficiency under varied distributional assumptions. To illustrate, we introduce one such estimator S_{bi} based on the biweight estimator of location, which uses the weight function $w(u) = (1 - u^2)^2$ for $|u| \leq 1$ and $w(u) = 0$ for $|u| > 1$. To compute S_{bi}, we first tabulate

$$u_i = \frac{X_i - \tilde{X}}{9MAD}.$$

Then we compute S_{bi}, summing over all values of i for which $|u_i| \leq 1$, from

$$S_{bi} = \frac{\sqrt{n \sum (X_i - \tilde{X})^2 (1 - u_i^2)^4}}{|\sum (1 - u_i^2)(1 - 5u_i^2)|}.$$

Although a computer program usually handles these details, we illustrate the computation of S_{bi} for the gear-teeth data. We have previously computed $\tilde{x} = 2263$ and $MAD = 53$. The remaining computations are outlined in Table 4.2. Substituting these values into the formula for S_{bi} yields the value 91.5. By comparison, for the same data we have $R = 473$, $s = 120.3$, and $R_F = 90$. The differences among these numerical values (including MAD and S_{bi}) mainly reflect differences in what the various estimators measure.

4.4 Efficiency of Scale Estimators

In comparing scale estimators we must take into account differences among their expected values. For example, in large samples $\text{E}(S) \approx \sigma$, whereas $\text{E}(MAD) \approx 0.6745\sigma$. Thus, we match the expected values of two estimators, S_1 and S_2, by finding a constant k that yields $\text{E}(S_1) = k\text{E}(S_2)$. Then the

Table 4.2

Computation of S_{bi} for the gear-teeth data.

i	x_i	$x_i - \tilde{x}$	u_i	$1 - u_i^2$	$(x_i - \tilde{x})^2$	$1 - 5u_i^2$
1	2431	168	.3522	.8760	28,224	.3798
2	2250	−13	−.0273	.9993	169	.9963
3	2311	48	.1006	.9899	2304	.9494
4	2210	−53	−.1111	.9877	2809	.9383
5	2329	66	.1384	.9809	4356	.9043
6	2263	0	.0000	1.0000	0	1.0000
7	2353	90	.1887	.9644	8100	.8220
8	2251	−12	−.0252	.9994	144	.9968
9	2275	12	.0252	.9994	144	.9968
10	2185	−78	−.1635	.9733	6084	.8663
11	1958	−305	−.6394	.5912	93,025	−1.0442

Note: $u_i = (x_i - \tilde{x})/(9MAD)$, $\tilde{x} = 2263$, $MAD = 53$.

---

usual approach to efficiency would compare $\text{Var}(S_1)$ and $k^2\text{Var}(S_2)$. Instead, we take an alternative approach that does not require us to determine k. We compare the variance of $\log(S_1)$ with the variance of $\log(S_2)$. This approach takes advantage of the fact that

$$\text{Var}[\log(kS_2)] = \text{Var}[\log(k) + \log(S_2)] = \text{Var}[\log(S_2)],$$

which does not depend on k. Thus we define the efficiency of S_1 relative to S_2.

$$E = 100\frac{\text{Var}[\log(S_2)]}{\text{Var}[\log(S_1)]}$$

The sample standard deviation is the most efficient scale estimator for random samples from the normal distribution. For this reason we compare the other scale estimators with S for normal data. In order to model the one-outlier case, we use the one-wild distributional situation, consisting of $n - 1$ random standard normal observations and one observation from $N(0, 100)$. For the one-wild situation the standard of comparison is the most efficient estimator available. Table 4.3 shows illustrative efficiency comparisons for samples of size 20.

From Table 4.3 we see that both MAD and R_F have about 40% efficiency relative to S in the normal case. The efficiency of S drops drastically to 11%

Table 4.3

Efficiency of selected estimators of scale in samples of size 20. The one-wild distributional situation consists of $n - 1$ random standard normal observations and one from $N(0, 100)$. Comparisons are with the most efficient estimator for each distributional case.

Estimator	Normal	One-Wild
S	100	11
MAD	35	41
R_F	41	47
S_{bi}	87	86

Source: Iglewicz, B. 1983. "Robust Scale Estimators and Confidence Intervals for Location." In D. C. Hoaglin, F. Mosteller, and J. W. Tukey, eds, *Understanding Robust and Exploratory Data Analysis*. New York: John Wiley & Sons. Entries from Table 12-6 on p. 418. Copyright ©1983, John Wiley & Sons, Inc. Reprinted by permission of John Wiley & Sons, Inc.

for the one-wild case, whereas that of MAD and R_F remains at about 40%. Thus, although S is highly efficient for normal random samples, it ceases to be a reliable estimator once the data may contain outliers. The efficiency of S_{bi} stays around 86% for both the normal and the one-wild distribution. This comparison demonstrates that estimators can be found with high efficiency under a variety of distributional assumptions. Such estimators have potential for a number of uses, including the detection of outliers.

4.5 Confidence Intervals

As described in Sections 4.1 and 4.2, trimmed means provide highly efficient estimators that accommodate outliers. Trimmed means also lead to confidence intervals for the population mean, quite similar to those based on $\bar{X}$. Consider the standard $100(1 - \alpha)\%$ confidence interval for μ, given by

$$\bar{X} \pm t_{n-1}(1 - \alpha/2)S/\sqrt{n},$$

where $t_{n-1}(1 - \alpha/2)$ is the $100(1 - \alpha/2)$ percentage point of the t distribution with $n - 1$ degrees of freedom. Patel et al. (1988) show that a $100(1 - \alpha)\%$ confidence interval can also be obtained by replacing $\bar{X}$ by T, replacing $S/\sqrt{n}$ by S_W, and using $n - 2r - 1$ degrees of freedom, where $2r$ is the number of observations trimmed. They obtain the standard error S_W from the *Winsorized variance*, according to

$$S_W^2 = \frac{\sum_{i=r+1}^{n-r}(X_{(i)} - T_W)^2 + r[(X_{(r+1)} - T_W)^2 + (X_{(n-r)} - T_W)^2]}{(n - 2r)(n - 2r - 1)},$$

where the corresponding Winsorized mean is

$$T_W = \frac{1}{n} \left\{ \sum_{i=r+1}^{n-r} X_{(i)} + r[X_{(r+1)} + X_{(n-r)}] \right\}.$$

(An alternative to trimming, the process of Winsorizing substitutes copies of $X_{(r+1)}$ and $X_{(n-r)}$ for the r observations that would be trimmed away at the low and high ends of the sample, respectively.) Thus, the alternative confidence interval is

$$T \pm t(1 - \alpha/2)S_W,$$

in which $t(1 - \alpha/2)$ now comes from the t distribution with $n - 2r - 1$ degrees of freedom. We would continue to trim about 15% from each end of the sample, as in Section 4.1.

To illustrate the computations required to obtain a 95% confidence interval, we again use the gear-teeth data. The results will show the benefits of basing the confidence interval on the trimmed mean when outliers are present. For this data set $\bar{x} = 2256$, $s = 120.3$, and $t_{10}(.975) = 2.228$. The customary 95% confidence interval for the population mean is (2175.1, 2336.9).

Next, consider the computation of the corresponding confidence interval based on the trimmed mean and Winsorized variance. Then for $n = 11$, trimming roughly 15% yields $r = 2$ and hence $n - 2r - 1 = 6$ degrees of freedom. A t table yields $t_6(.975) = 2.447$. The value of T has been previously computed as 2269.86. Now to find T_W and S_W, we need the ordered observations.

$$1958 \; 2185 \; 2210 \; 2250 \; 2251 \; 2263 \; 2275 \; 2311 \; 2329 \; 2353 \; 2431$$

Then

$$\begin{aligned} T_W &= [(2210 + 2250 + 2251 + 2263 + 2275 + 2311 + 2329) \\ &\quad + 2(2210 + 2329)]/11 = 2269.73, \end{aligned}$$

and so

$$\begin{aligned} S_W^2 &= \left\{ \sum_{i=3}^{9}(x_{(i)} - 2269.73)^2 + 2(2210 - 2269.73)^2 \right. \\ &\quad \left. + \; 2(2329 - 2269.73)^2 \right\} /[(7)(6)] = 565.6691. \end{aligned}$$

The resulting 95% confidence interval is (2211.7, 2328.1). Notice that this interval, with width 116.4, is considerably shorter than the customary interval (width 161.8), even though the t value used to obtain this interval is larger than the one used to compute the usual 95% t confidence interval.

This example illustrates that trimmed means yield straightforward confidence intervals for the population mean. A simple computer program can make it easier to obtain such intervals in practice. Intervals based on suitable trimmed means are safer to use when the sample may contain outliers.

Robust confidence intervals offer another important advantage. The temptation occasionally exists to remove suspicious extreme observations and calculate the usual confidence interval from the remaining data. This practice can lead to the removal of good data, thus resulting in narrower intervals than are warranted. Equivalently, this practice results in an underestimate of σ. The systematic procedure for a robust interval takes into account the possibility that some observations may be set aside, and it avoids subjective elements. Rocke (1992) discusses this topic further.

4.6 Summary

One or more outliers can cause considerable damage to classical estimates of location and scale. In discussing a few estimators that can accommodate outliers, we have given special attention to the trimmed mean, which is easy to compute and has high efficiency, relative to the mean, under a variety of distributional assumptions. The trimmed mean also leads to confidence intervals that are only slightly more difficult to compute than the usual t intervals, and are superior when outliers are present.

We also considered a number of scale estimators. The sample standard deviation S becomes inefficient when outliers are present. The biweight estimator of scale S_{bi} has good efficiency, both when the data are normal and when outliers are present. The resistant estimators are more reliable for comparing variability between populations, when the samples have the potential of containing outliers.

5

Outlier Identification

Numerous formal tests, at specified significance levels, have been proposed for identifying outliers. Barnett and Lewis (1984) give details and discuss most of the better-known procedures. Here, we consider several of those tests, review their properties, and make recommendations. In this chapter we draw on results for data (other than the outliers) that come from a normal distribution, because the normal distribution serves most frequently as the theoretical model for random samples. Tests for outliers from the normal distribution are readily available and simple to use. They also frequently help identify the "true" outliers. A screening device may yield false positives, however, and so these methods may identify observations falsely as outliers, especially when the underlying distribution has heavier tails than the normal.

5.1 Two Popular Tests

In order to illustrate key concepts, we first consider two popular tests, the extreme studentized deviate and the L_r test. We do not recommend these, but modified versions of them are among the best tests for detecting outliers in normally distributed samples. These two tests illustrate the properties that a good test should have.

The training data set,

$$2.1 \quad 2.6 \quad 2.4 \quad 2.5 \quad 2.3 \quad 2.1 \quad 2.3 \quad 2.6 \quad 8.2 \quad 8.3$$

(introduced in Section 3.1) will serve throughout this chapter to illustrate the numerical computations for each test. Any reasonable outlier identification procedure should easily detect the two clear outliers, 8.2 and 8.3.

5.1.1 The Extreme Studentized Deviate Test

The test based on the extreme studentized deviate (ESD) is quite good at detecting one outlier in a random normal sample. We declare x_j to be an outlier when

$$T_S = \max_i \{|x_i - \bar{x}|/s : i = 1, \ldots, n\}$$

exceeds a tabled critical value, and we denote by x_j the observation that leads to the largest $|x_i - \bar{x}|/s$. In principle, if T_S does not exceed the critical value, we need not pick out x_j. Assuming this test finds an outlier, we then test for further outliers by removing observation x_j and repeating the process on the remaining $n - 1$ observations.

For the training data set, $\bar{x} = 3.540$, $s = 2.489$, and the values of $|x_i - \bar{x}|/s$ are

$$0.579, \ 0.378, \ 0.458, \ 0.418, \ 0.498, \ 0.579, \ 0.498, \ 0.378, \ 1.872, \ 1.913.$$

Thus $T_S = 1.913$. Table A.1 (see appendix) gives the critical values for a general version of this procedure that can test for up to r outliers. Because we are testing for only one outlier, we use the second column of this table, which corresponds to $r = 1$. The entry for $r = 1$ and $\alpha = .05$ gives the critical value 2.290. Because $1.913 < 2.290$, mechanical use of this test without looking at the data would lead us to conclude that the sample contains no outliers.

What went wrong? A second outlier, 8.2, hid the effect of 8.3 by keeping T_S from getting too large. This phenomenon, called *masking*, affects a number of popular tests for identifying outliers. Masking occurs when discordant observations cancel the effect of more extreme observations and prevent an outlier-detection procedure from declaring any of the observations to be outliers. Masking is not a problem when the outlier-identification test is based on estimators with high breakdown points. In any event, good outlier-identification procedures should have little trouble with masking.

To illustrate that T_S works well for detecting one outlier, we remove the 8.3 from the data set. Then $T_S = 2.6$, and the 5% critical value equals 2.215. The test now detects the one remaining outlier, 8.2.

5.1.2 The L_r Test

As an alternative, it is possible to test simultaneously for r outliers, possibly following the use of a data-labeling rule. Tietjen and Moore (1972) introduced such a procedure. For our data set, their test can verify whether the two largest observations are truly outliers. The test statistic for detecting r upper outliers is

$$L_r = \frac{\sum_{i=1}^{n-r}(x_{(i)} - \bar{x}_r)^2}{\sum_{i=1}^{n}(x_{(i)} - \bar{x})^2},$$

where $\bar{x}_r$ is the sample mean obtained after removing the r largest observations. The r observations are then declared to be outliers if L_r is *less* than the critical value. The critical region consists of small values, because removing outliers reduces the size of the sum of squares in the numerator. A test for r lower outliers can be performed in an analogous manner. For our example, $L_2 = 0.005$, whereas the 5% critical value equals 0.233. Thus, 8.2 and 8.3 are both declared to be outliers.

The L_r test has the drawback that it is susceptible to *swamping*, which can occur when the r suspected observations actually contain r^* true outliers and $r - r^*$ values that should not be declared outliers. The r^* true outliers can make L_r small enough that all r suspected observations appear to be outliers.

To illustrate swamping, consider the gear-teeth data, which contain the outlier 1958. Suppose that someone mistakenly feels that the two smallest observations are outliers and decides to use the test analogous to L_r with $r = 2$. In this situation we need to remove the two smallest observations from the numerator instead of the two largest observations. Then $L_2 = 40,326.8/159,302 = 0.2531$. The 5% critical value is 0.270. Because $0.2531 < 0.270$, the two smallest observations are declared outliers, even though the 2185 is not discordant and does not have any other features that would cast suspicion on it.

How can we tell whether an outlier-identification procedure is working well? The observation 1958 seems to be a true outlier. The L_2 test identified this outlier. At the same time, the L_2 test identified a false outlier. Our interpretation of how well the test performed depends on the criterion we use. Assuming that the sample contains r true outliers, we have three possible criteria.

5.1.3 Performance Criteria

1. $\Pr(r$ observations are declared outliers$)$.

2. $\Pr(\text{the } r \text{ true outliers are identified})$.

3. $\Pr(\text{exactly } r \text{ outliers are found, and they are the true ones})$.

Although all three criteria are based on r outliers, they differ considerably. Criterion 1 states that r observations are declared outliers, irrespective of whether they are true outliers. Criterion 2 states that the r true outliers are identified without specifying whether any false outliers are also detected. Criterion 3 is more conservative; it states that all the true outliers are identified and no false outliers are found.

Many other measures of test performance are possible, as Beckman and Cook (1983) discuss in more detail. They also mention the error rate,

$$\text{Error Rate} = E_1/(E_1 + E_2),$$

where E_1 is the expected number of false outliers found, and E_2 is the expected number of true outliers found. This measure combines the expected number of false and true outliers into a single criterion. In an average sense, a procedure's error rate indicates the fraction of the outliers it finds that are false.

5.2 Selected Outlier-Identification Tests

We next discuss five carefully chosen outlier-identification procedures. These procedures include several that we highly recommend. They also illustrate four philosophical approaches to constructing such tests. One approach assumes that there are up to r outliers and then identifies a subset of $r_1 \leq r$ outliers. The generalized ESD procedure is such a test. Another approach first tests for one outlier and, if found, removes this observation and continues such testing until the test statistic for the reduced sample is no longer significant. The Shapiro-Wilk test and procedures based on b_2 and T_S are examples of this approach. An alternative approach guesses the number and location of all outliers and then performs an appropriate test that simultaneously determines whether this block of observations can be declared outliers. The Tietjen and Moore procedure and the Dixon tests belong to this type. Yet another approach uses a single test statistic once to determine simultaneously all outliers without specifying the number or location in advance. Rules based on the modified boxplot have this form.

5.2.1 Generalized ESD Many-Outlier Procedure

By modifying the extreme studentized deviate procedure T_S, one can test for up to a prespecified number r of outliers. First compute $R_1 = (\max_i |x_i - \bar{x}|)/s$. Then find and remove the observation that maximizes $|x_i - \bar{x}|$. Compute R_2 in the same way as R_1, but from the reduced sample of $n-1$ observations. Continue this process until $R_1, R_2, \ldots, R_r$ have all been computed. Using the critical values λ_i at, say, the 5% significance level from Table A.1, find l, the maximum i such that $R_i > \lambda_i$. The extreme observations removed at the first l steps are then declared to be outliers.

Rosner (1983) discusses this procedure in some detail. The two-sided $100\alpha\%$ critical values in Table A.1 come from the formula

$$\lambda_i = \frac{t_{n-i-1,p}(n-i)}{\sqrt{(n-i-1+t^2_{n-i-1,p})(n-i+1)}},$$

where $i = 1, \ldots, r$, $t_{\nu,p}$ is the $100p$ percentage point from the t distribution with ν degrees of freedom, and $p = 1 - [\alpha/2(n-i+1)]$. Rosner (1983) shows that this approximation is reasonably accurate for the entries given in Table A.1, and is very accurate when $n > 25$.

We now illustrate the generalized ESD procedure for our hypothetical training data set. Let us assume that there are no more than $r = 3$ outliers. The ensuing computations and actions are summarized in Table 5.1, with λ_i, for $\alpha = .05$, obtained from Table A.1. Table 5.1 shows that $R_1 < \lambda_1$, $R_2 > \lambda_2$, and $R_3 < \lambda_3$. Thus, 2 is the largest i such that $R_i > \lambda_i$, and the test declares 8.2 and 8.3 to be outliers. The removal of the second outlier results in a sizable reduction of $\bar{x}$, from 3.01 to 2.36. This change illustrates again the influence of outliers on the value of $\bar{x}$. Of even greater interest is the tenfold drop in s from $s = 1.96$ to $s = 0.20$, reminding us how much more sensitive s is to the presence of outliers in the sample.

32

Table 5.1

Required computations for generalized ESD procedure.

i	Stage 1		Stage 2		Stage 3	
	x_i	$|x_i - \bar{x}|/s$	x_i	$|x_i - \bar{x}|/s$	x_i	$|x_i - \bar{x}|/s$
1	2.1	0.579	2.1	0.466	2.1	1.315
2	2.6	0.378	2.6	0.210	2.6	1.190
3	2.4	0.458	2.4	0.312	2.4	0.188
4	2.5	0.418	2.5	0.261	2.5	0.689
5	2.3	0.498	2.3	0.364	2.3	0.313
6	2.1	0.579	2.1	0.466	2.1	1.315
7	2.3	0.498	2.3	0.364	2.3	0.313
8	2.6	0.378	2.6	0.210	2.6	1.190
9	8.2	1.872	8.2	2.654	–	–
10	8.3	1.913	–	–	–	–
Maximum		1.913		2.654		1.315
λ_i		2.290		2.215		2.127

The choice of r plays an important role in this test. In general, only a few outliers are suspected, allowing the use of relatively small values of r, say $r = 3$. When in doubt, we choose r on the high side, because too low a value can result in failure to identify true outliers. As we mentioned earlier, this difficulty can arise when the sample contains more than r outliers or from the potential for masking when r is chosen too small. Selecting a larger value of r than needed does require additional computation, but it has minimal effect on the chance of identifying false outliers.

The generalized ESD procedure is quite easy to use, even with a hand-held calculator. It requires only an upper bound on the number of outliers, a value that can be chosen somewhat higher than anticipated. This procedure works well under a variety of conditions. For these reasons, we highly recommend the generalized ESD procedure when testing for outliers among data coming from a normal distribution.

5.2.2 Test Based on the Sample Kurtosis

The sample kurtosis

$$b_2 = \frac{n \sum_{i=1}^{n} (x_i - \bar{x})^4}{(\sum_{i=1}^{n} (x_i - \bar{x})^2)^2}$$

has long been used to test for outliers and measure departures from normality. This statistic is quite easy to compute and use. Initially, b_2 is compared with the critical value for the appropriate n and α. Table A.2 (see appendix), from D'Agostino and Tietjen (1971), gives the 10%, 5%, and 1% critical values for selected sample sizes, $7 \leq n \leq 50$. Percentage points of b_2 for $n > 50$ are given in Pearson and Hartley (1966). If b_2 exceeds the critical value, then the observation x_j that maximizes $|x_i - \bar{x}|$ is declared an outlier. This observation is then removed, and the procedure is repeated.

Our hypothetical training data set again serves to illustrate this method. For this data set, $b_2 = 3.23$. The corresponding 5% critical value ($n = 10$), from Table A.2, is 3.95. Because $b_2 < 3.95$, the process stops with no outliers detected.

Although b_2 was unable to detect 8.2 and 8.3 as outliers, the sample kurtosis is a reasonable procedure to use in practice. It is, however, susceptible to masking when neighboring outliers are present. This issue is carefully discussed by Hampel (1985). To avoid masking, Jain (1981) suggested using b_2 in a fashion analogous to the generalized ESD procedure and supplied the appropriate critical values for such a test. We prefer the generalized ESD procedure because it is easier to compute by hand, and the individual ESD values measure the deviations from the reduced sample mean.

5.2.3 The Shapiro-Wilk W Test

Shapiro and Wilk (1965) introduced a test for normality that has attractive features in testing for outliers. In fact, they build on theoretical results that show how to combine the order statistics $X_{(1)}, X_{(2)}, \cdots, X_{(n)}$ of a sample from $N(\mu, \sigma^2)$ into an estimator for σ that has the form $\sum_{i=1}^{n} c_i X_{(i)}$. Specifically, they compute

$$b = \sum_{i=1}^{h} a_{n+1-i}(X_{(n+1-i)} - X_{(i)}),$$

where h is the largest integer that does not exceed $n/2$ (i.e., $h = n/2$ if n is even, and $h = (n-1)/2$ if n is odd), and the coefficients a_{n+1-i} come from a special table in Shapiro (1986) and several other sources. The pair of order statistics $X_{(i)}$ and $X_{(n+1-i)}$ contributes to b through $X_{(n+1-i)} - X_{(i)}$ because of the symmetry of the normal distribution. Thus, in effect, the coefficient of $X_{(i)}$, which lies below the median of the sample, has the same magnitude and the opposite sign as the coefficient of $X_{(n+1-i)}$, the corresponding order statistic above the median. Also, the difference $X_{(n+1-i)} - X_{(i)}$ allows μ to cancel out, leaving only σ. In a sense, each of the differences $X_{(n+1-i)} - X_{(i)}$ is an estimator of σ. The coefficients a_{n+1-i} weight these estimators together, taking into account the correlations among them and the differing variability of the order statistics.

The test for normality, known as the *W test*, compares b^2 to $D = \sum_{i=1}^{n}(X_i - \bar{X})^2$, another estimator of σ^2, which we recognize as $(n-1)S^2$. The procedure involves the following steps.

1. Define $h = n/2$ for n even and $(n-1)/2$ for n odd; obtain the constants a_{n+1-i} for $i = 1, 2, \cdots, h$ (from Shapiro (1986) or Barnett and Lewis

(1984)); and calculate

$$b = \sum_{i=1}^{h} a_{n+1-i}(x_{(n+1-i)} - x_{(i)}).$$

2. Compute $D = \sum_{i=1}^{n}(x_i - \bar{x})^2$.

3. Compute $W = b^2/D$.

4. Declare that no outliers are present if $W > C$, where the critical value C is available in a number of sources, including Shapiro (1986) and Barnett and Lewis (1984). Otherwise, regard the most deviant observation from $\bar{x}$ as the outlier. Remove this observation, and repeat the process on the reduced sample.

In this test the critical region contains small values of W, because an outlier has less impact on b^2 than on D.

For the hypothetical training data set, $n = 10$ and $h = 5$. The constants required are $a_{10} = .5739$, $a_9 = .3291$, $a_8 = .2141$, $a_7 = .1224$, and $a_6 = .0399$. Then

$$b = .5739(6.2) + .3291(6.1) + .2141(.3) + .1224(.3) + .0399(.1) = 5.671.$$

Next, $D = 55.744$, $W = (5.671)^2/55.744 = .577 < .842$. The 5% critical value equals .842, and the 1% critical value is .781. Thus 8.3 is declared an outlier.

After removing 8.3 we get

$$b = .5888(6.1) + .3244(.5) + .1976(.3) + .0947(.2) = 3.832$$

and $D = 30.569$. Thus $W = (3.832)^2/D = .480$. The 5% critical value equals .829 (and the 1% critical value is .764), so 8.2 is declared an outlier. The observation 8.2 is then removed, and the value of W is computed from the remaining 8 observations. This step leads to $W = .901$, which is to be compared with the 5% critical value for $n = 8$, namely .818. Thus, the W test identifies 8.2 and 8.3 as outliers.

Overall, the generalized ESD test performs better in identifying outliers than the Shapiro-Wilk W test. The W test is also clumsier to use, because one needs h different constants for each value of n. The W procedure, however, remains useful for its primary purpose, testing whether a sample seems to follow a normal distribution. Thus it needs to be sensitive to a variety of departures from normality, much broader than the presence of outliers in the sample.

5.2.4
Dixon-Type
Tests

Tests of the Dixon type work with ratios of ranges of parts of the ordered sample. The flexibility of this structure gives rise to many procedures, each designed to detect a specific pattern of suspected outliers. In the discussion that follows, $\lambda_{j,k-1}$ denotes the appropriate critical value for the procedure of type $r_{j,k-1}$ with critical values given in Table A.3 (see appendix).

Test for a single outlier on the right. Declare $x_{(n)}$ an outlier if

$$r_{11} = \frac{x_{(n)} - x_{(n-1)}}{x_{(n)} - x_{(2)}} > \lambda_{11}.$$

Generally, the tests of type $r_{j,k-1}$ divide $x_{(n)} - x_{(n-j)}$ by $x_{(n)} - x_{(k)}$ for some j and k not much greater than 1. We choose $k = 2$ in order to guard against potential effects of masking caused by an outlier at the left end of the sample. A single outlier on the left can similarly be tested by first taking the negative of each observation and then performing the test. This works because letting $y_i = -x_i$ implies that $y_{(n+1-i)} = -x_{(i)}$.

Test for two outliers on the the right. Declare both $x_{(n)}$ and $x_{(n-1)}$ outliers if

$$r_{21} = \frac{x_{(n)} - x_{(n-2)}}{x_{(n)} - x_{(2)}} > \lambda_{21}.$$

The corresponding test for two outliers on the left works with the negative of each observation.

Test for one outlier on either side. Use the rule to declare either the smallest or the largest observation to be an outlier if

$$r'_{10} = \max \left[\frac{x_{(n)} - x_{(n-1)}}{x_{(n)} - x_{(1)}}, \frac{x_{(2)} - x_{(1)}}{x_{(n)} - x_{(1)}} \right] > \lambda'_{10}.$$

As an illustration, the hypothetical training data set seems to have two outliers on the right. Then

$$r_{21} = \frac{x_{(n)} - x_{(n-2)}}{x_{(n)} - x_{(2)}} = \frac{8.3 - 2.6}{8.3 - 2.1} = .92.$$

This value is to be compared with $\lambda_{21} = .612$, obtained from the 5% column of Table A.3. Since $.92 > .612$, this test declares both 8.3 and 8.2 to be outliers.

The Dixon-type tests are very easy to use, but the results depend heavily on choosing correctly the exact number and location of all suspected outliers. Thus, these tests are susceptible to the possibility of either swamping or masking. For this reason, we recommend the Dixon tests only for very small samples, when only one or at most two outliers are considered. We feel that the generalized ESD procedure is preferable for larger samples. Those who wish to use Dixon tests may first use the standard boxplot to determine the location of suspected observations and then use the appropriate Dixon procedure, when outside values are found, to test for significance. (A purist might object that starting with the boxplot alters the significance level of the test. Often, however, we require only that the test give a reasonable indication of whether the suspected observations are outliers.)

5.2.5 The Boxplot Rule

The standard boxplot, introduced in Section 3.4, has upper and lower fences, respectively, defined as

$$U = Q_3 + 1.5(Q_3 - Q_1) \text{ and } L = Q_1 - 1.5(Q_3 - Q_1).$$

Values falling outside the fences are considered potential outliers. This rule has a higher chance of detecting false outliers than is typical in a formal test. Hoaglin and Iglewicz (1987) obtained appropriate replacements for the multiplicative constant 1.5 that ensure that a random normal sample has a prespecified probability of containing no outside values. These constants are reproduced as Table A.4 (see appendix). For example, for $n = 10$, replacing 1.5 by 2.4 yields a boxplot rule that has probability .95 of containing no outside values when the data are random normal samples. For larger values of n, the appropriate value of the constant is roughly 2.3.

For the hypothetical training data set, $Q_3 - Q_1 = 2.6 - 2.3 = 0.3$, and $2.4(0.3) = 0.72$. Thus, $U = 2.6 + 0.72 = 3.32$, and $L = 2.3 - 0.72 = 1.58$. Observations outside the interval $(1.58, 3.32)$ are considered outliers. Thus, the boxplot rule (at 5%) simultaneously identifies 8.2 and 8.3 as outliers.

The boxplot rule is equivalent to a Dixon-type test. To see this, assume that, for a particular value of k from Table A.4, x is outside the upper cutoff value. Then $Q_3 + k(Q_3 - Q_1) < x$. Equivalently,

$$\frac{x - Q_3}{Q_3 - Q_1} > k.$$

The corresponding rule for a lower outlier is

$$\frac{Q_1 - x}{Q_3 - Q_1} > k.$$

The boxplot rule is simple to use and does not require preliminary knowledge of the number of outliers in the sample. As a consequence, this rule can be placed in standard packages as a routine procedure that screens for outliers. The entries of Table A.4, additionally, provide for a better understanding of the relationship between k and the probability that a random normal sample contains no observations that are outside. This information can give additional insight to those using the standard boxplot as an outlier-labeling rule. As a possible drawback, the rule is less powerful than some of the alternative outlier-identification procedures discussed in this chapter.

Table 5.2

Comparison of five outlier-identification procedures for normal samples of size 20.

| | Case 1 | | | | | Case 2 | | | | |
| | Procedure | | | | | Procedure | | | | |
x	Box	b_2	ESD	SW	Dix	Box	b_2	ESD	SW	Dix
3.0	17	19	23	12	16	24	17	28	14	21
3.5	36	46	51	27	37	44	38	57	33	45
4.0	56	73	78	50	62	64	61	82	56	69
4.5	73	90	93	71	82	79	80	95	76	86
5.0	86	98	99	88	93	90	91	99	90	95
5.5	94	100	100	96	98	96	97	100	97	99
6.0	98	100	100	99	100	99	99	100	99	100
6.5	99	100	100	100	100	100	100	100	100	100
7.0	100	100	100	100	100	100	100	100	100	100
	Case 3					Case 4				
	Procedure					Procedure				
x	Box	b_2	ESD	SW	Dix	Box	b_2	ESD	SW	Dix
3.0	9	4	23	25	9	19	20	16	3	7
3.5	22	14	50	49	24	38	49	41	12	15
4.0	39	33	77	73	45	57	77	70	27	29
4.5	58	57	92	89	66	74	93	89	49	43
5.0	74	78	98	97	82	87	98	97	71	60
5.5	86	91	100	99	91	94	100	100	87	74
6.0	94	97	100	100	96	98	100	100	95	86
6.5	97	99	100	100	99	99	100	100	99	92
7.0	99	100	100	100	99	100	100	100	100	96

Notes: Entries show the percentage of 5000 simulated samples in which x was declared an outlier. Methods are based on the adjusted boxplot (Box); kurtosis statistic (b_2); generalized extreme studentized deviate (ESD); Shapiro-Wilk test (SW); and Dixon test with location of outliers decided by standard boxplot (Dix). Case 1 consists of 19 random standard normal observations and 1 at x. The other cases have 18 random standard normal observations. Case 2 has 1 additional observation at x and 1 at 0. Case 3 has 2 at x. Case 4 has 1 at x and 1 at $-x$.

We now ask how well the five procedures can identify true outliers. To make such comparisons, we must choose an appropriate measure of performance. As background for our choice, we briefly review two general approaches to samples containing two outliers.

5.3
Comparison of
the Five
Outlier-
Identification
Procedures

First, a number of investigators have used simulation. They start with synthetic random samples from the standard normal distribution and modify them by adding the values c_1 and c_2, respectively, to the last two observations. Thus, they use a variant of the location-shift model described in Section 2.3. This approach has the drawback that the perturbed two observations may occasionally not be outliers. For example, a random observation from $N(4, 1)$, corresponding to $c_1 = 4$, may actually equal 2.5, which is not an outlier by the definition used here. The location-shift model, however, does correspond to a class of mechanisms that may arise in practice.

Second, to study how outlier-identification procedures respond to configurations of the sample that contain up to two outliers, Prescott (1978) drew contour lines for the location of two points, x and y, that correspond to a significant value of the test statistic at the usual significance levels. The remaining $n - 2$ observations were the expected values of the standard normal order statistics in a sample of $n - 2$. The resulting contour plot provides an informative summary of a procedure's performance. For example, the limiting cases $y = x$ and $y = -x$ may reveal whether the procedure has problems with masking. A possible limitation of the approach arises from its use of the expected order statistics; absence of any random element may yield too much regularity. As a consequence, the contour plots may not apply directly to the performance of tests with real data.

We have taken an intermediate approach by constructing synthetic samples from $n - k$ random normal observations and k fixed constants, which can be varied to produce outliers. The goal is to estimate the probability with which a procedure identifies the outliers at specified positions. Table 5.2 gives the results for $n = 20$ and $k = 1$ or 2, with $x = 3(0.5)7$ and different relationships between y and x. In order to observe the behavior of each test under varied conditions of masking, we include four cases.

1. The sample consists of 19 standard normal observations plus 1 fixed constant x, which moves between 3 and 7. This case models the 1-outlier situation.

2. The sample consists of 18 standard normal observations plus 1 observation at 0 and 1 at a point x, which moves between 3 and 7. The 0 models the situation where the standard is known, resulting in a tendency to place some readings closer to the standard. This case also contains an outlier.

3. The sample consists of 18 standard normal observations plus 2 outliers, x and x (that is, $y = x$). This case models the two-outlier situation with the outliers close to each other.

39

4. The sample consists of 18 standard normal observations plus 2 outliers, one at x and the other at $-x$ (that is, $y = -x$). This case models the situation where the 2 outliers are at opposite ends of the sample.

Five thousand random samples were generated on the Temple University Cyber 860 computer using the IMSL subroutine GGNML. For each sample, we set up all four cases and computed the results as we stepped the value of x. The entries in Table 5.2 give the proportion of the 5000 samples in which the outlier x was detected. In this way we compare the five procedures discussed in Sections 5.2.1 to 5.2.5: the generalized ESD many-outlier procedure, the test based on the sample kurtosis, the Shapiro-Wilk test, the Dixon-type test (after using the standard boxplot to guess the direction and number of possible outliers), and the boxplot rule.

The main conclusions of this investigation are as follows:

- An observation needs to be about five standard deviations from the population mean to be declared an outlier with a high degree of certainty. For example, if the data come from the $N(18, 4)$ distribution, then the value 25 would most likely not be declared an outlier, whereas 28 would. Thus, observations declared to be outliers by common outlier-identification procedures are noticeably discordant.

- The modified boxplot rule has lower power than the generalized ESD procedure for normal samples. Its advantage is ease of use and a graphical description of the outliers. A recent investigation by Brant (1990) shows that this rule's performance becomes competitive with that of the generalized ESD procedure when the distribution deviates slightly from the normal.

- Each of the five procedures (Sections 5.2.1 to 5.2.5) is capable of identifying x as an outlier as long as x is sufficiently large.

- Although the Shapiro-Wilk procedure does perform well, overall the generalized ESD procedure performs better. In addition, the Shapiro-Wilk test requires a table of approximately $n/2$ constants for each sample size n. This test, however, is still quite good for testing for normality under varied alternative conditions, the task for which it was designed.

- Use of the standard boxplot to label the outliers, followed by a confirmatory Dixon-type test, is inferior to the generalized ESD rule when multiple outliers are present.

- The b_2 rule (sample kurtosis) performs reasonably well and is especially powerful when the sample has outliers on each side.

- The generalized ESD procedure works especially well and can be recommended for general use.

40

The overall conclusions from Table 5.2 are that the generalized ESD procedure works well under the varied conditions used for constructing that table. We highly recommend this rule. The Dixon-type rules, though, can be recommended for very small samples, when the location of the potential outliers can be determined by inspection. Finally, we note that the percentage points for these procedures reflect somewhat different assumptions for each test. For example, the kurtosis procedure is based on finding an outlier, removing that observation, and then recomputing the statistic. The generalized ESD procedure, on the other hand, gives an overall error rate that measures the chance of falsely classifying an entire set of outliers. As a consequence, the entries of Table 5.2 would change slightly if the percentage points for these procedures were to be computed under more uniform assumptions.

5.4 Summary

We have discussed a number of outlier-identification procedures from among the many in the literature. Some of these procedures are highly susceptible to either masking or swamping. Such outlier-identification procedures are not recommended. Other procedures not recommended require specific knowledge of the number and location of the outliers. The generalized ESD procedure performs especially well under each of the conditions. It is also relatively easy to compute and interpret. We recommend this procedure highly, from the results in Table 5.2 and from conclusions reached in other studies. Alternatively, a Dixon-type test is sometimes useful for very small samples.

6

Outliers from Non-Normal Univariate Distributions

As discussed in Chapter 5, outlier-identification procedures for normal data are relatively easy to use and quite powerful. The normal distribution is a reasonable approximation for many data distributions because it is unimodal and symmetric and has moderate tails. Outliers from the normal show up as sizable deviations from the mean.

Many univariate data sets, however, do not resemble a normal distribution. Of particular interest are data that exhibit noticeable skewness. Then such families as the gamma, lognormal, and Weibull distributions may provide a better fit to the data. If so, the normal outlier-identification techniques of Chapter 5 can falsely identify extreme observations as outliers. Removing the more extreme observations will tend to distort the data toward symmetry and a closer resemblance to the normal distribution.

Statistical methods have been developed for identifying outliers from most of the common non-normal distributions. We will concentrate on the heavily used lognormal and exponential families, including censored exponential situations. Barnett and Lewis (1984) discuss outliers from other distributions. In some situations a transformation makes the data close to normal and allows the techniques of Chapter 5 to identify the outliers. Any outliers identified in this way depend on the practical justification for the particular transformation.

6.1 Lognormal Distribution

Many practical situations yield data that are highly skewed, usually to the right. In such situations, a lognormal distribution is frequently more appropriate than a normal distribution. This family of distributions bears the name *lognormal* because, in the simplest case, the logarithms of the observations follow a normal distribution. That is, if X is a random variable from a lognormal distribution, then $Y = \log_e(X)$ has a normal distribution. The mean of this normal distribution controls the scaling of X, and the variance determines the degree of skewness. The inverse relationship $X = e^Y$ shows how a symmetric distribution can be transformed into one that is skewed to the right. A more general form of the lognormal distribution includes a

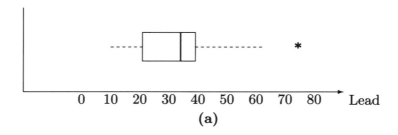

(a)

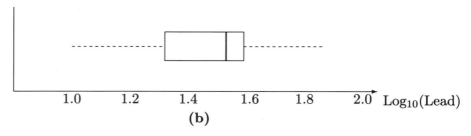

(b)

Figure 6.1. Concentration of lead (μg/dl) in blood of exposed children. Shown in a, boxplot of the raw data; b, boxplot of the logarithms of the data. $*$ = outlier.

location parameter θ to handle data that are displaced to the right of zero, as in $X = \theta + e^Y$. Johnson and Kotz (1971, Chapter 14) give a summary of the lognormal distribution.

In occupational and environmental data especially, relatively large deviations from the mean are common. When such data are assumed to come from a normal distribution, the extreme values may erroneously be considered outliers. Data from Morton et al. (1982) provide an illustration. These data give the level of lead in the blood (in μg/dl) of 33 children who were at greater risk for exposure to lead because their fathers worked at a battery-manufacturing plant. These lead levels were compared (in matched pairs) with those of 33 neighboring children whose parents did not work in such a plant. The data for the unexposed children seem to follow a normal distribution with no outliers. We focus on the data from exposed children.

10	13	14	15	16	17	18	20	21	22	23
23	24	25	27	31	34	34	35	35	36	37
38	39	39	41	43	44	45	48	49	62	73

Figure 6.1a shows a boxplot of these data. This boxplot labels one observation, 73, as an outlier. Should we investigate it further? From Figure 6.1a

we notice that the data appear to be skewed. Because other types of occupational and environmental data more nearly follow a lognormal distribution (Shumway 1989), we consider transforming these data.

Figure 6.1b gives the boxplot of the logarithms of the data. This boxplot has no outside values, and the dashed lines extending out from the box have nearly equal length. Thus, the data do not seem to contain outliers. We may tentatively regard these data as closer to a lognormal distribution than to a normal distribution, but in the log scale the fourths are still not close to symmetry about the median. This pattern invites us to investigate these data further, and we do so in Section 6.4.

This example illustrates that a transformation of the data may affect our decision to flag some of the observations as outside. The reason is that the cutoff points (Section 3.4) are defined in terms of the quartiles, Q_1 and Q_3, and a nonlinear transformation changes the relative spacing among the quartiles and observations that are not close to them. For example, in the original scale the data have (using the definition in Section 3.4) $Q_1 = 21$ and $Q_3 = 39$, so that the upper cutoff point is $Q_3 + 1.5(Q_3 - Q_1) = 66$, and the observation 73 lies beyond it. In the log scale (base 10), however, we have $Q_1 = 1.32$, $Q_3 = 1.59$, and $Q_3 + 1.5(Q_3 - Q_1) = 1.99$, whereas $\log_{10} 73 = 1.86$. Thus, it may be possible, by an artful choice of transformation, to reshape the data in such a way that actual outliers no longer appear to be outside. When we transform data, however, we aim to improve the analysis as a whole (e.g., by making the whole sample more nearly symmetric or by making the distribution more nearly normal), and we strongly prefer transformations that have a sensible interpretation in the context of the data. Outside observations may call attention to the need for a transformation (e.g., because they form part of a pattern of skewness); but they do not, by themselves, guide the choice of the transformation.

6.2 Exponential Distribution

Industrial statisticians frequently deal with data that measure time to failure or length of life. Such data are typically skewed and are often modeled by a Weibull distribution, whose best-known special case is the exponential. The exponential distribution plays a key role for survival and extreme-value data because many of its mathematical properties are known, it often approximates such data reasonably well, and relatively simple transformations relate the exponential distribution to a number of other distributions. Therefore, techniques for identifying outliers in exponential data can be used after performing an appropriate transformation.

For an exponential distribution with parameter λ, the density and distribution function can be written as

$$f(x) = \frac{1}{\lambda} e^{-x/\lambda} \text{ and } F(x) = 1 - e^{-x/\lambda},$$

respectively. If X follows this distribution, then $E(X) = \lambda$, and $\text{var}(X) = \lambda^2$. The standard exponential distribution has $\lambda = 1$.

The more general Weibull distribution has distribution function

$$F(x) = 1 - \exp\left[-\left(\frac{x-a}{b}\right)^r\right], \ r > 0, \ b > 0, \ x > a,$$

and this reduces to an exponential distribution (with an additional parameter) when $r = 1$. If the random variable X follows this Weibull distribution, then $Y = [(X-a)/b]^r$ has a standard exponential distribution.

We next consider a relatively simple test for detecting multiple outliers in data that, except for the outliers, come from an exponential distribution. The test extends the Cochran procedure for detecting an upper outlier from the exponential distribution, which uses the critical region

$$\frac{X_{(n)}}{\sum_{i=1}^{n} X_{(i)}} > K.$$

We illustrate the Cochran test with the simple hypothetical data set $\{2, 4, 7, 10, 32\}$, which is assumed to come from an exponential distribution. To test whether the largest observation in a sample of 5 is an outlier, we use the 5% critical value 0.6838 (Barnett and Lewis 1984, p. 369). For these data $x_{(5)} = 32$ and

$$\frac{x_{(5)}}{\sum_{i=1}^{5} x_{(i)}} = 32/55 = 0.5818 < 0.6838;$$

perhaps surprisingly, we have insufficient evidence to declare the value 32 an outlier.

Kimber (1982) adapted the generalized ESD many-outlier procedure to develop a test for up to r upper outliers from the exponential distribution. The approach first chooses r (the maximum number of outliers) and then removes the largest observations from the upper end of the sample, starting with the largest r (i.e., $X_{(n+1-r)}, X_{(n+2-r)}, \ldots, X_{(n)}$) and decreasing the number of observations being removed until only outliers are removed. Specifically, for $j = 1, 2, \ldots, r$ Kimber defines the test statistic S_j by

$$S_j = \frac{X_{(n+1-j)}}{\sum_{i=1}^{n+1-j} X_{(i)}}.$$

Then, for $j = r, r-1, \ldots, 1$ we ask whether $S_j > s_j$, where s_j is the appropriate critical value from Table A.5. The largest value of j, say r^*, for which $S_{r^*} > s_{r^*}$ declares the upper r^* observations as outliers. That is, this test works from the inside out.

Kimber's test is very easy to use, and Bendre and Kale (1985) have shown that it is competitive with other procedures for this situation. They found that the test has reasonable power for detecting outliers from a scale-shift model. For example, at the 5% significance level the probability of detecting two outliers from an exponential distribution with $\lambda = 10$, when the other 18 random observations come from an exponential with $\lambda = 1$, is 0.7.

Two numerical examples illustrate this procedure. The following data, from Nelson (1982, p. 252), represent the time (in seconds) to breakdown of insulating fluid at voltages of 30kV and 40kV. Nelson states that "such a distribution of time to breakdown is usually assumed to be exponential in engineering theory." Assuming an exponential distribution, are there any outliers?

30kV	40kV
50	1
134	1
187	2
882	3
1450	12
1470	25
2290	46
2930	56
4180	68
15,800	109
29,200+	323
86,100+	417

We consider first the 40kV data, in which the last two numbers seem high. Let us test for up to two upper outliers; that is, we use $r = 2$ with $n = 12$. Then the 5% critical values are $s_1 = .427$ and $s_2 = .372$, and the required calculations give

$$\sum_{i=1}^{11} x_{(i)} = 646 \text{ and } S_2 = 323/646 = 0.500.$$

Because $S_2 > s_2$, we declare the data points 323 and 417 to be outliers.

Next, the 30kV data appear to contain as many as three upper outliers. In the last two entries of this data set the "+" signs indicate that the observations are censored. This means that the fluid did not break down by that time, when measurements ceased. We discuss censored data in the next section. The present example shows that the censored observations cause no difficulty when we do not need to work with their numeric values. The critical values for $n = 12$ and $r = 3$ are not available, so we use an approximation. Kimber (1982) sets

$$\binom{n}{j} [(1 - s_j)/(1 + js_j - s_j)]^{n-j} = \alpha/r,$$

where α is the significance level and s_j the corresponding critical value. Solving for s_j yields

$$s_j = \frac{1-U}{1+(j-1)U}, \text{ where } U = \left[(\alpha/r) / \binom{n}{j} \right]^{\frac{1}{n-j}}.$$

For $n = 12$, $r = 3$, and $\alpha = .05$, this approximation gives $s_3 = 0.384$. For the 30kV data, then,

$$\sum_{i=1}^{10} x_{(i)} = 29,373, \text{ and } S_3 = 15,800/29,373 = 0.538 > 0.384,$$

and so we declare the three largest observations $15,800$, $29,200+$, and $86,100+$ as outliers.

These two data sets, consisting of 24 observations, seem to contain a total of 5 outliers. The most plausible explanation is that the data do not come from exponential distributions, but rather from some quite different source, perhaps another member of the Weibull family. Blind use of the exponential distribution for these two data sets can lead to invalid estimates of the parameters and to misleading conclusions. In this instance rejection of the exponential distribution seems to be the chief benefit of the tests for outliers. Nelson (1982) noticed this and investigated other distributions as models for these two data sets.

We have concentrated on upper outliers, as these are usually the most troublesome in practice. Sometimes, however, the smallest observations seem suspicious, and far less energy has been devoted to them. A version of the Cochran test uses the smallest observation in the numerator instead of the largest observation. Another choice consists of repeated application of the Shapiro-Wilk test for exponential data, which can be used to test for both upper and lower outliers. Barnett and Lewis (1984) give detailed discussions of such tests.

6.3 Censored Data

Censored data frequently occur in practice, especially among reliability measurements of time to failure or human survival data. One source of censoring is the need to terminate the period of observation after a specified duration or at a certain time of day. This type of censoring is called *right-censoring*: the (unknown) actual observation is at least as large as the value recorded. Both right-censoring and left-censoring may occur, for example, in a failure study that must terminate after an eight-hour shift and where failure times during the first hour are recorded only at the end of that hour. Censoring can also occur because of the limitations of the measuring instrument; for example, an instrument can measure carbon monoxide only up to 100 parts per million. We have already encountered censored data in the breakdown times for insulating fluid at 30kV, but this case was especially simple because the two censored observations happened to be the two largest values, and neither censored observation was used in the final outlier decision. Matters become far more complex when censored observations occur within the body of the data. At present we have no definite rules for identifying outliers among censored data, although a recent boxplot-type outlier-labeling procedure by Kimber (1990) can be helpful.

Censored data require special care because an otherwise innocent-looking observation can cause more damage to an estimate than a more noticeable outlying observation. Gillespie (1989), for example, shows that the estimated empirical distribution function typically undergoes a greater change when the censoring code (+) is misread as failure than when the observed value is recorded incorrectly. As a consequence, data errors need not appear as outliers; but careful scrutiny for outliers will eventually identify the source of such persistent errors and lead to a correction of the problem.

For some situations involving censored data, Kimber uses the standard boxplot of Section 3.4. If the lower and upper quartiles are Q_1 and Q_3, respectively, we let $R_F = Q_3 - Q_1$. Then observations within the interval $(Q_1 - 1.5R_F, Q_3 + 1.5R_F)$ are considered inside, and all observations outside this interval are labeled as potential outliers.

As an illustration we consider again the data on breakdown of insulating fluid at 30kV. For these data $Q_1 = (187 + 882)/2 = 534.5$, $Q_3 = (4180 + 15,800)/2 = 9990$, and $R_F = 9455.5$. Then the outlier cutoffs are at $534.5 - 1.5(9455.5)$ and $9990 + 1.5(9455.5)$. Because the data cannot be negative, the lower cutoff produces no outside values. The upper cutoff, at 24,173, leads us to label the two censored observations, $29,200+$ and $86,100+$, as outliers. This result differs from the previous analysis, which declared the three largest observations as outliers, but that investigation assumed an exponential distribution.

This approach does not work when censored observations occur in the interior of the ordered sample, as the ordered values will not be available to compute the quartiles. An empirical distribution function $\hat{F}(x)$ of time to failure can, however, be obtained and used to estimate the quartiles. Kimber suggests using the Kaplan-Meier (1958) product-limit estimator for $\hat{F}$. To compute this estimator, we first order the observations; and then for the ith ordered observation $x_{(i)}$ we compute

$$\hat{F}(x_{(i)}) = 1 - \prod_{j=1}^{i} \left[\frac{n-j}{n-j+1} \right]^{\delta_j},$$

where $\delta_j = 0$ for a censored observation and 1 for an uncensored observation. For estimating the quartiles, we use linear interpolation for $\hat{F}$ between ordered observations.

To illustrate the required computations, consider the five observations $2, 6+, 8+, 10,$ and 25. The following table gives the value of the empirical distribution function at the uncensored data values.

x	i	$\prod[\frac{n-j}{n-j+1}]^{\delta_j}$	$\hat{F}(x)$
2	1	$4/5 = .8$	.2
10	4	$.8(1/2) = .4$	.6
25	5	0	1.0

The next step is to estimate Q_1 and Q_3. If we were working with the true distribution function $F(x)$, we would solve for the values of x at which $F(x) = .25$ and $F(x) = .75$, respectively. We would like to do the same with $\hat{F}(x)$. Technically, $\hat{F}(x)$ is constant between the observed (uncensored) values of x, and at those points it jumps. The available values of $\hat{F}$ in this instance allow us to estimate Q_1 and Q_3 more smoothly by linear interpolation. Thus, we get

$$Q_1 = 2 + \frac{.25 - .2}{.6 - .2}(10 - 2) = 3$$

and

$$Q_3 = 10 + \frac{.75 - .6}{1.0 - .6}(25 - 10) = 15.625.$$

From these and $R_F = 12.625$ we obtain the cutoffs $3 - 1.5(12.625) = -15.94$ and $15.625 + 1.5(12.625) = 34.56$. Thus, these data do not appear to contain outliers.

Although these calculations are somewhat tedious, a simple computer program can handle them. In summary, censored observations do occur, and some tools are available for identifying possible outliers in such data. Additional discussions regarding the handling of censored industrial data can be found in Nelson (1982).

6.4 Transformations to Normality

Many data sets are highly skewed or in other respects depart from the normal distribution. Often a suitable mathematical transformation can reshape the data so that they more nearly resemble observations from a normal distribution. Such a transformation may help in determining the distribution of the original data, making possible the selection of appropriate statistical procedures for estimation and testing.

Skewness, the most common departure from normality, is quite easy to detect. One possible goal is a transformation that helps symmetrize the data, and the resulting transformed data then typically come closer to being normally distributed. Here we briefly discuss one approach for finding such a transformation. Because it does not depend on the extreme observations, this approach is not affected by potential outliers. Specifically, the procedure, discussed by Emerson and Stoto (1983, p. 105–111), uses the *letter values*, which we define below.

Consider a data set of size n, with the ordered observations $x_{(1)} \leq x_{(2)} \leq \cdots \leq x_{(n)}$. Define the depth of the median as $d_1 = (n+1)/2$, the depth of the fourths as $d_2 = (\lfloor d_1 \rfloor + 1)/2$, the depth of the eighths as $d_3 = (\lfloor d_2 \rfloor + 1)/2$, and so on. Here $\lfloor d_1 \rfloor$, for example, indicates the greatest integer $\leq d_1$. For $j \geq 2$ the jth letter values are the pair of ordered observations with depth d_j from each end. That is, they are $x_{(d_j)}$ and $x_{(n+1-d_j)}$, respectively. Tukey (1977, Section 2G) defined the letter values and introduced single-letter names for them: F for the fourths, E for the eighths, D for the sixteenths, and so on backward through the alphabet. In the present development we use $\tilde{x}$ for the median. We also use x_L and x_U, respectively, for the lower and upper letter values in a pair (when we do not need to specify the particular pair). The difference between $(x_L + x_U)/2$ and $\tilde{x}$ measures skewness.

Consider the family of power transformations, indexed by $p \neq 0$.

$$y = \frac{x^p - 1}{p}$$

In the limit as $p \to 0$, this transformation approaches the function $y = \ln x$. We now write the family of transformations in the equivalent simpler form

$$y = \begin{cases} x^p & \text{if } p \neq 0 \\ \ln x & \text{if } p = 0 \end{cases}$$

Emerson and Stoto (1983) provide a guide for choosing p. They compute p for each pair of letter values from the equation

$$\frac{x_L + x_U}{2} - \tilde{x} = (1 - p) \left[\frac{(x_U - \tilde{x})^2 + (\tilde{x} - x_L)^2}{4\tilde{x}} \right].$$

They then choose a round value close to the median of the computed estimates of p as the exponent to be used in the power transformation. This method works well if the p's are close to each other; otherwise, it provides only a rough guide to the appropriate transformation.

We now illustrate the approach for the blood-lead data of Section 6.1. Because these are occupational data, we started with a logarithmic transformation ($p = 0$), as at least a form of first aid. As an alternative, we determine p by using the method of Emerson and Stoto. Table 6.1 gives the required computations.

The conclusions from Table 6.1 are quite surprising, as they suggest transformation by $y = x^2$, which differs considerably from $y = \ln x$. Indeed, $y = x^2$ goes in the opposite direction from $y = \ln x$. The dotplots of Figure 6.2 help answer whether either the quadratic or the log transformation makes practical sense. In Figure 6.2a, the dotplot of the original data suggests that the observations may form two main clumps, with two possible outliers at the right. It seems likely that the children of the battery workers were exposed to different amounts of lead. Squaring the data (Figure 6.2b) makes the outliers stand out, and the higher clump looks more spread out than the lower clump. By contrast, the logarithmic transformation (Figure 6.2c) pulls in the outliers (they seem almost to belong to the higher clump), and it makes the lower

51

clump look noticeably skewed to the left. Thus, the lognormal distribution does not provide a reasonable model for these data. We would leave the data in the original scale and seek further information on the children that might distinguish the two clumps. For example, their fathers' jobs in the battery plant might involve different levels of exposure to lead.

In summary, we started by looking for outliers in the blood-lead data. Besides having an outlier or two, these data actually seem to be a mixture, perhaps reflecting the duties of the fathers. In their careful study, Morton et al. (1982) went considerably further. They defined three categories of the father's potential exposure to lead (high, medium, or low), according to the job functions at the battery plant. They also classified each worker's practices of personal hygiene as good, moderately good, or poor, reflecting the degree of compliance with the recommended procedure of showering, shampooing, and changing clothes and shoes before leaving work. Thus, we could conceivably see as many as nine groups, although the data are spread too thinly for such a detailed pattern to emerge. We can say that the two apparent outliers, 73 and 62, came from children whose fathers had jobs involving high potential exposure to lead and whose fathers' personal hygiene was rated poor. On a positive note, for the three children whose fathers had high exposure but good hygiene, the mean level of blood lead was only slightly greater than that in the control group.

Table 6.1

Calculation of the power p for a power transformation that would make the data on blood-lead levels symmetric at three pairs of letter values (selected quantiles). Median: $\tilde{x} = 34$.

Letter Value	Depth	x_L	x_U	w	z	$1-p$	p
F	9	21	39	−4.0	1.426	−2.8	3.8
E	5	16	45	−3.5	3.272	−1.1	2.1
D	3	14	49	−2.5	4.596	−0.5	1.5

Note: $w = \frac{x_L + x_U}{2} - \tilde{x}$ and $z = \frac{(x_U - \tilde{x})^2 + (\tilde{x} - x_L)^2}{4\tilde{x}}$.

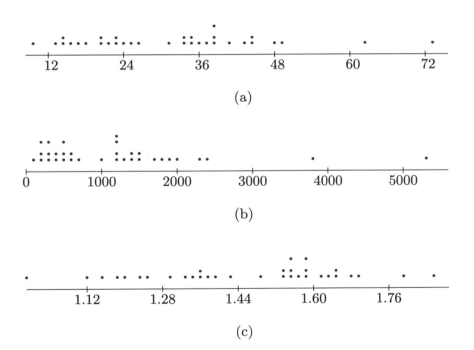

(a)

(b)

(c)

Figure 6.2. The blood-lead levels in the original scale and two transformed scales. Shown in a, dotplot of the raw data; b, dotplot of the squared data; c, dotplot of the logarithms of the observations.

7

Outliers in Linear Regression

Most analyses of (x, y) data involve fitting a regression line $\hat{y} = a + bx$ to summarize the relationship between the dependent variable y and the explanatory variable x. Sometimes the analyst first transforms y or x or both (by a function such as the logarithm or the square root) in order to make the pattern more nearly straight. Outliers in (x, y) data may take more forms than in univariate data, and detecting them offers more challenges. In univariate data we need only look at the two ends of the sample. By contrast, a set of (x, y) data may contain observations that are outliers on y, outliers on x, or incompatible with the apparent relationship between y and x (without being outliers on either x or y). The situation is more challenging because some (x, y) data points have more impact than others on the fitted regression line. We approach these possibilities first and foremost by plotting the data. In addition, we have specialized diagnostic techniques; and we may use a robust method, instead of least squares, to fit a line.

To illustrate these ideas, we consider a hypothetical set of 10 observations:

x	7.4	7.7	7.6	7.9	7.1	7.3	10.0	7.8	13.0	7.2
y	7.4	7.7	7.6	7.9	7.1	7.3	5.0	7.8	13.3	7.2

The pattern of these data resembles one encountered in a study that compared carbon monoxide readings from inexpensive dosimeters with readings from an accurate, but far more expensive, carbon monoxide monitor. The range of the hypothetical data, however, does not imitate the actual carbon monoxide readings, which were between 25 and 100 parts per million. The hypothetical data have another artificial feature: 8 of the 10 observations have $y = x$. Actual data would generally show far more variability.

A plot of these data, Figure 7.1a, shows three key features.

- The bulk of the data (the 8 observations at the left) lie on a straight line.

- The point $(13, 13.3)$, although clearly an outlier on both x and y, lies close to the line determined by those 8 points.

- The point $(10, 5)$, also an outlier on both x and y (but less so than $(13, 13.3)$), lies far from the line.

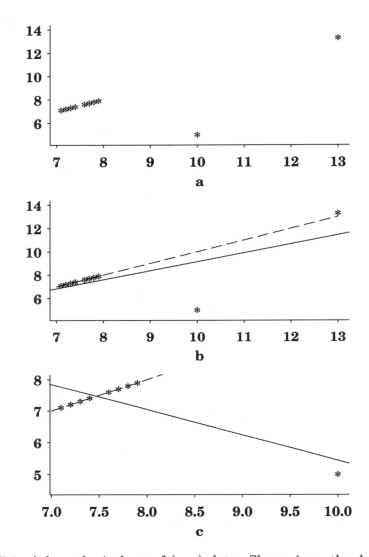

Figure 7.1. A hypothetical set of (x, y) data. Shown in a, the data; b, the data with the least-squares line (solid) and a robust line (dashed); c, the data and the two fitted lines after removing the point $(13, 13.3)$.

Thus, having an outlying value of x or of y or of both x and y does not, by itself, mark an observation as a source of trouble for the regression line. Indeed, the point $(13, 13.3)$ is beneficial, because it suggests that the straight-line relationship between y and x holds over a wider range of x. Thus, a numerical measure that alerts us to the presence of possible outliers from a simple regression should focus attention on the point $(10, 5)$. Also, we would like to be aware of points like the one at $(13, 13.3)$, even though they do not seem discrepant.

To look numerically at how the individual data points depart from a regression line, it is customary to calculate the fitted values

7.1 Leverage and the Hat Matrix

$$\hat{y}_i = a + bx_i$$

and the residuals

$$e_i = y_i - \hat{y}_i.$$

One hopes that a large residual (especially relative to its standard error) will signal the presence of each outlier. Unfortunately, an outlier need not produce a large residual. The difficulty arises when that observation has disproportionate impact on the regression line, causing $\hat{y}_i$ to be close to y_i. To describe the impact of an observation, we can look at a standard formula for the slope of the least-squares line

$$b = \frac{\sum_{i=1}^{n}(x_i - \bar{x})y_i}{\sum_{i=1}^{n}(x_i - \bar{x})^2}.$$

If we hold all the x_i fixed and vary a single y-value, the greatest change in b will come when the magnitude of $x_i - \bar{x}$ is greatest. Importantly, the formula for b also shows that each y_i contributes (unless the corresponding x_i happens to equal $\bar{x}$).

In the hypothetical example, $\bar{x} = 8.3$. Thus the two points with greatest impact on b are $(13, 13.3)$ and $(10, 5)$. In fact, the point $(10, 5)$ has enough impact to produce $b = 0.769$, instead of $b \approx 1$ as we would expect from the other observations.

For a numerical measure of potential impact, it is useful to focus on the contribution of y_i to the corresponding fitted value $\hat{y}_i$. In the centered form the regression line is $\hat{y} = \bar{y} + b(x - \bar{x})$; in particular,

$$\hat{y}_i = \bar{y} + b(x_i - \bar{x}).$$

Now we replace b by the standard formula given above, so that

$$\hat{y}_i = \bar{y} + (x_i - \bar{x})\frac{\sum_{j=1}^{n}(x_j - \bar{x})y_j}{\sum_{k=1}^{n}(x_k - \bar{x})^2}.$$

Substituting $\bar{y} = (1/n) \sum_{j=1}^{n} y_j$ and rearranging then give

$$\hat{y}_i = \sum_{j=1}^{n} \left\{ \frac{1}{n} + \frac{(x_i - \bar{x})(x_j - \bar{x})}{\sum_{k=1}^{n}(x_k - \bar{x})^2} \right\} y_j.$$

The expression inside the braces does not depend on any y-values; it involves only values of x.

We now denote that expression by h_{ij}. Thus, we may write

$$\hat{y}_i = \sum_{j=1}^{n} h_{ij} y_j,$$

in which h_{ij} indicates how changing y_j affects $\hat{y}_i$. Together, the h_{ij} form the symmetric $n \times n$ *hat matrix* $\mathbf{H} = (h_{ij})$, described by Hoaglin and Welsch (1978). To measure the potential impact of y_i on $\hat{y}_i$, we define the *leverage* of observation i as h_{ii}, the corresponding diagonal element of the hat matrix. From this development we see that, for the simple regression line,

$$h_{ii} = \frac{1}{n} + \frac{(x_i - \bar{x})^2}{\sum_{k=1}^{n}(x_k - \bar{x})^2}.$$

Hoaglin and Welsch (1978) and Hoaglin (1988) mention a number of properties of the hat matrix and its diagonal elements h_{ii}.

- $0 \leq h_{ii} \leq 1$ (for any linear regression).

- Whenever the regression includes the constant (intercept) term (as simple linear regression does), $(1/n) \leq h_{ii} \leq 1$.

- In simple linear regression, $\sum_{i=1}^{n} h_{ii} = 2$ (unless all the x_i are equal), and hence the average size of an h_{ii} is $2/n$.

- If $h_{ii} = 0$ or $h_{ii} = 1$, then $h_{ij} = 0$ for all $j \neq i$.

For the hypothetical data, Table 7.1 gives h_{ii} for each data point. Not surprisingly, observation 9 has $h_{ii} = .820$. By contrast, the h_{ii} for observation 7 is not much larger than those for the other eight observations. Here the average size of h_{ii} is $2/10 = .2$. We should not, however, jump to the conclusion that all the observations except observation 9 have below-average leverage. Because $\sum h_{ii} = 2$, the other h_{ii} must share a total of only $2 - .820 = 1.180$. Also, the term $1/n$ contributes .1 to each h_{ii}. Thus, in this instance, with only 10 observations, the presence of one observation with very high leverage tends to push the other h_{ii} together. When we look at those nine h_{ii} as a group, we can see that the h_{ii} for observation 7 stands out as somewhat higher than the rest.

Both graphically and numerically we may ask when an observation has high leverage. Graphically, the formula for h_{ii} shows that, in the plot of y

Table 7.1

Leverage and Residuals in the Hypothetical Data Set

i	x_i	y_i	h_{ii}	e_i	RSTUDENT$_i$
1	7.4	7.4	.126	.26	.16
2	7.7	7.7	.112	.33	.20
3	7.6	7.6	.116	.31	.19
4	7.9	7.9	.105	.38	.23
5	7.1	7.1	.147	.19	.12
6	7.3	7.3	.133	.24	.15
7	10.0	5.0	.194	−4.14	−291.81
8	7.8	7.8	.108	.35	.22
9	13.0	13.3	.820	1.86	7.85
10	7.2	7.2	.139	.22	.13

versus x, the points with high leverage have x_i relatively far away from $\bar{x}$ (in the hypothetical data $\bar{x} = 8.3$). Numerically, it is often helpful to have a rule, and Huber (1981, p. 162) offers the following simple and convenient criterion.

> Values of $h_{ii} \leq 0.2$ appear to be safe, values between 0.2 and 0.5 are risky, and if we can control the design at all, we had better avoid values above 0.5.

Again in terms of the formula for h_{ii}, an observation in simple regression has high leverage when it single-handedly accounts for a large enough fraction of $\sum (x_i - \bar{x})^2$ or when n is small enough. Hoaglin (1988) discusses an interpretation of Huber's criterion in terms of the mean of a sample of m independent observations with $m = 1/h_{ii}$. Ordinarily we prefer to avoid fitted values $\hat{y}_i$ that behave as if they are based on only a small part of the data. A large h_{ii} means that $\hat{y}_i$ must lie close to y_i, whatever value y_i may take. In the hypothetical data observation 9 clearly has high leverage, but y_9 lies close to the line determined by the left-most eight points, so its contribution does not displace $\hat{y}_9$.

Huber's criterion helps us to identify observations that have increased leverage so that we can investigate them further. In practice, however, no single criterion seems to handle all patterns of leverage. Thus, we often examine the h_{ii} as a batch to see whether any stand out.

In the remainder of the present discussion we abbreviate h_{ii} to h_i. When we are not considering the full hat matrix, we do not need the repeated subscript.

7.2 Deletion and Studentized Residuals

Leverage helps to explain the inadequacy of the ordinary residuals $e_i = y_i - \hat{y}_i$ for detecting outliers. The higher h_i is, the closer $\hat{y}_i$ is to y_i. Thus, points of high leverage produce artificially small residuals. As a partial remedy we calculate $\hat{y}_i$ from the other $n-1$ observations, deleting observation i. Deletion forms the basis for a powerful approach to regression diagnostics because simple formulas yield all the necessary ingredients, without actually removing each observation in turn and redoing the regression calculations.

To denote a quantity calculated from the data without observation i, we attach "(i)" (read "not i" or "i omitted"). For example, $\hat{y}_i(i)$ is the predicted y-value at x_i when the regression is fitted to the data without observation i, and $b(i)$ is the corresponding slope. Thus, we have

$$\hat{y}_i(i) = \bar{y}(i) + b(i)[x_i - \bar{x}(i)],$$

and suitable algebraic manipulation yields the shortcut formula

$$y_i - \hat{y}_i(i) = \frac{e_i}{1 - h_i}.$$

As an aid in spotting outliers we ordinarily express residuals on a standard scale (e.g., a scale in which everything has mean 0 and variance 1). The process has two ingredients. First, if each y_i is assumed to have variance σ^2, then the variance of e_i is $\sigma^2(1 - h_i)$. Second, as an estimate of σ^2 we use the residual mean square

$$s^2 = \sum_{i=1}^{n} e_i^2 / (n-2).$$

Thus, the usual estimate of the variance of e_i is $s^2(1-h_i)$, and dividing by the square root of this quantity yields the *standardized residual* $e_i/(s\sqrt{1-h_i})$. Straightforward use of the standardized residuals, however, encounters two complications. First, as we mention above, a point of high leverage has an artificially small e_i. Second, a large e_i can inflate s^2 and thus make the standardized residual smaller, so that it may not reveal the outlier. We reduce these complications by using quantities other than e_i and s^2.

To get a form of residual that is more helpful in spotting observations with discrepant y-values, we start with the predicted residual $y_i - \hat{y}_i(i)$ which has variance $\sigma^2/(1 - h_i)$. In estimating this variance, we replace s^2 by $s^2(i)$, the residual mean square from the regression without observation i, which we can obtain from the shortcut formula

$$(n-3)\, s^2(i) = (n-2)\, s^2 - \frac{e_i^2}{1 - h_i}.$$

Thus, we divide the predicted residual by the square root of its estimated variance to obtain the *studentized residual*

60

$$\text{RSTUDENT}_i = \frac{e_i}{s(i)\sqrt{1 - h_i}}.$$

This definition has the advantage that, when the fluctuation in y follows a normal distribution, an individual RSTUDENT_i follows Student's t distribution on $n - 3$ degrees of freedom, so that we can examine the studentized residuals in a familiar scale. An individual studentized residual, chosen without regard for its value, will lie above $+2$ or below -2 only roughly 5% of the time. Of course, the studentized residuals that attract attention are the largest in magnitude, and so wider limits apply.

The right-hand column of Table 7.1 gives the studentized residuals for the hypothetical data set. From the plot of y against x in Figure 7.1a, we already expect RSTUDENT_7 to have a large negative value, but -292 exceeds our wildest dreams. Part of the reason lies in the fact that the y-values involve almost no variation about the regression line when observation 7 is removed. Thus, $s(7)$ is much smaller than we would expect in practice. Even with a more typical value of $s(7)$, however, RSTUDENT_7 would still be large, calling attention to the outlier.

The ordinary residual $e_9 = 1.86$, by contrast, inflated by the effect of observation 7 on the line, gets a boost by a factor of more than 2 from $\sqrt{1 - h_i} = \sqrt{1 - .82}$ in the denominator of RSTUDENT_9 and a further boost from $s(9)$. Even though observation 9 has high leverage, however, it is not an outlier, relative to the line determined by the left-most eight points.

If we approached the calculation of $y_9 - \hat{y}_9(9)$ mechanically and actually fitted the least-squares line to the data without observation 9, we would get $\hat{y} = 13.5 - 0.805x$, Figure 7.1c. The negative slope reveals how much observation 7 is able to twist the line in the absence of observation 9. This outcome serves to warn of a more general problem with diagnostic measures that leave out only one observation. Two (or more) discrepant observations may each affect the line in such a way that the numerical measure reveals the true situation only when both observations are removed. One remedy involves fitting the line by a robust method that can tolerate the presence of a reasonable number of discrepant data points. We discuss selected robust methods in Section 7.4, after a brief look at leverage and studentized residuals in multiple regression.

7.3 Multiple Regression

In some (x, y) data the relation of y to x may follow a pattern more complicated than a straight line and thus may require further terms in the fit to describe it. For example, we might have

$$\hat{y} = b_0 + b_1\,x + b_2\,x^2.$$

The definitions of leverage and studentized residuals readily extend to cover a wide variety of regression models. We now discuss those generalizations in the customary framework of multiple regression.

61

The multiple regression model relates y to the p explanatory variables or carriers $X_1, X_2, \ldots, X_p$ through an equation such as

$$y_i = b_1 x_{i1} + b_2 x_{i2} + \cdots + b_p x_{ip} + e_i,$$

in which the b_j are the fitted regression coefficients, x_{ij} are the individual values of X_j, and (as before) e_i is the residual. Here we choose not to write the constant term separately as b_0. Instead, we include it as one of the regression coefficients, for two reasons. First, we have chosen to use p for the number of carriers, and we prefer to number them from 1 to p, rather than from 0 to $p - 1$. Second, the notation reminds us that the constant term involves both a coefficient (one of the b_j) and a carrier (one of the X_j), even if each individual value x_{ij} of that carrier is 1. Most commonly X_1 is the constant carrier.

Often one writes a multiple regression equation more compactly in matrix notation. For example, in

$$\mathbf{y} = \mathbf{Xb} + \mathbf{e}$$

the y_i form the $n \times 1$ vector $\mathbf{y}$, the x_{ij} form the $n \times p$ matrix $\mathbf{X}$, $\mathbf{b}$ is the $p \times 1$ vector of regression coefficients, and $\mathbf{e}$ is the vector of residuals. We assume that $\mathbf{X}$ has full rank p.

The vector of least-squares regression coefficients can be written in terms of $\mathbf{X}$ and $\mathbf{y}$ as

$$\mathbf{b} = (\mathbf{X}^T\mathbf{X})^{-1}\mathbf{X}^T\mathbf{y}.$$

Substituting this expression for $\mathbf{b}$ in the vector of fitted values

$$\hat{\mathbf{y}} = \mathbf{Xb}$$

yields

$$\hat{\mathbf{y}} = \mathbf{X}(\mathbf{X}^T\mathbf{X})^{-1}\mathbf{X}^T\mathbf{y}.$$

To emphasize the linear relationship between $\hat{y}_i$ and the y_j, we define

$$\mathbf{H} = \mathbf{X}(\mathbf{X}^T\mathbf{X})^{-1}\mathbf{X}^T$$

and write

$$\hat{\mathbf{y}} = \mathbf{H}\mathbf{y}.$$

Just as in simple regression, $\mathbf{H}$ is the *hat matrix*, and its elements h_{ij} have the same interpretation. The average of the h_i is p/n, and Huber's criterion still applies.

For the studentized residuals the formula remains

$$\text{RSTUDENT}_i = \frac{e_i}{s(i)\sqrt{1 - h_i}},$$

but now $s(i)$ comes from the more general formula

$$(n - p - 1)\, s^2(i) = (n - p)\, s^2 - \frac{e_i^2}{1 - h_i}.$$

When the fluctuations in the y_i follow a normal distribution, RSTUDENT_i has a t distribution on $n - 1 - p$ degrees of freedom. Thus, in multiple regression we continue to identify outliers by looking for observations that have large studentized residuals.

Conveniently, the studentized residuals and the diagonal elements of the hat matrix are available in popular statistical software. Without attempting to give detailed coverage of this rapidly changing area, we mention three systems: Data Desk (registered trademark of Data Description, Inc.), Minitab (registered trademark of Minitab, Inc.), and SAS (registered trademark of SAS Institute, Inc.).

Even when we fit a multiple regression to (x, y) data, a plot of y versus x still enables us to see the details of the relationship. More general multiple regression situations can offer greater challenges in identifying outliers and diagnosing influential data. The books by Atkinson (1985), Belsley, Kuh, and Welsch (1980), Myers (1990), and Cook and Weisberg (1982) and the review paper (with discussion) by Chatterjee and Hadi (1986) describe and compare a sizable number of diagnostic measures.

7.4 Robust Simple Regression

The various diagnostic measures aim at enabling the user of least-squares regression to cope with the fact that all observations, no matter how discrepant, have an impact on the regression line (or, more generally, on the multiple regression). Robust methods adopt a different approach, akin to outlier accommodation (Chapter 4). They try to give a fitted line (technically, no longer "the regression line") that is unaffected by arbitrarily discrepant behavior of a limited number of the data points. Statistical researchers have devised a considerable variety of techniques for robust line fitting. Emerson and Hoaglin (1983) give a detailed exposition of the three-group resistant line from exploratory data analysis and also describe several other techniques. The book by Rousseeuw and Leroy (1987) discusses more-recent developments and devotes a special effort to making robust regression available for everyday statistical practice. The present section uses one simple robust method to illustrate the main idea.

As long as the two points (x_i, y_i) and (x_j, y_j) do not have $x_i = x_j$, they can determine a straight line, whose slope we denote by b_{ij}

$$b_{ij} = \frac{y_j - y_i}{x_j - x_i}.$$

Table 7.2

Fitting the repeated-median line to the hypothetical data set.

a. Pairwise slopes, b_{ij}, $i < j$ (Those not shown equal 1.)

$b_{1,7} = -0.923$, $b_{1,9} = 1.054$
$b_{2,7} = -1.174$, $b_{2,9} = 1.057$
$b_{3,7} = -1.083$, $b_{3,9} = 1.056$
$b_{4,7} = -1.381$, $b_{4,9} = 1.059$
$b_{5,7} = -0.724$, $b_{5,9} = 1.051$
$b_{6,7} = -0.852$, $b_{6,9} = 1.053$
$b_{7,8} = -1.273$, $b_{7,9} = 2.767$, $b_{7,10} = -0.786$
$b_{8,9} = 1.058$
$b_{9,10} = 1.052$

b. First-stage medians (Those not shown equal 1.)

$\text{med}_{j \neq 7}\{b_{7j}\} = -0.923$, $\text{med}_{j \neq 9}\{b_{9j}\} = 1.056$

c. Second-stage median

$b_{RM} = \text{med}_i\{\text{med}_{j \neq i}\{b_{ij}\}\} = 1$

d. $a_i = y_i - b_{RM}x_i$ (Those not shown equal 0.)

$a_7 = -5.0$, $a_9 = 0.3$
$a_{RM} = \text{med}_i\{a_i\} = 0$

e. Fitted line

$\hat{y}_{RM}(x) = a_{RM} + b_{RM}x = x$

f. Residuals

i	1	2	3	4	5	6	7	8	9	10
$y_i - \hat{y}_{RM}(x_i)$	0	0	0	0	0	0	-5	0	0.3	0

For simplicity we assume that the x_i are distinct; then we have $n(n-1)$ pairwise slopes, counting both b_{ij} and b_{ji}. From these pairwise slopes Siegel's (1982) repeated-median procedure derives a single slope b_{RM} in two stages, first taking the median at each point and then taking the median across points

$$b_{RM} = \text{med}_i\{\text{med}_{j \neq i}\{b_{ij}\}\}.$$

That is, the first stage takes the median of the slopes of the $n-1$ lines that pass through the point (x_i, y_i), and the second stage takes the median of these n resulting slopes. To get an intercept a_{RM} for the line, we calculate $a_i = y_i - b_{RM}x_i$ $(i = 1, 2, \cdots, n)$ and then take

$$a_{RM} = \text{med}_i\{a_i\}.$$

Almost half the data points can be wild without making either b_{RM} or a_{RM} wild.

The hypothetical data set provides a ready illustration of the benefit of fitting a robust line. Table 7.2 shows the calculations for the repeated-median line. The special structure of the data enables us to present the details compactly by, for example, listing only those b_{ij} that do not equal 1. Briefly, the repeated-median line for these data

$$\hat{y}_{RM}(x) = x$$

does exactly what we want a robust line to do. It passes through the left-most eight points and leaves nonzero residuals only at observations 7 and 9, as shown in Figure 7.1b. We can notice, from Figure 7.1c, that removal of point 9 has no effect on the robust line, whereas it drastically changes the slope of the least-squares line.

Relative to the least-squares line, a robust regression line will tend to produce more residuals of small magnitude, more large residuals, and fewer medium-sized residuals. In checking for outliers we would ordinarily treat the residuals from a robust line as a univariate sample and apply the exploratory outlier-labeling rule discussed in Section 3.4 or perhaps one of the formal outlier-identification methods from Chapter 5. Either approach should serve us well.

We have not tried to develop an analog to the studentized residuals for use with a robust line, for two reasons. First, the robustness generally makes the leave-out-one approach unnecessary. We expect deletion of one observation to have little effect on a robust line, so we can use the ordinary residual, rather than a predicted residual. Similarly, if we wished to divide each residual by a measure of scale of the residuals, we would use a robust measure, such as a constant multiple of the *MAD* (Section 4.3), which would change little with the deletion of any single observation. Second, we do not yet have theoretical results on the relative variability of the residuals from a typical robust line, as given for the least-squares residuals by $\mathrm{Var}(e_i) = \sigma^2 (1 - h_i)$. It would be reasonable to expect, however, that a robust method's lower sensitivity to high-leverage observations would tend to produce residuals that have more nearly constant variability. Thus, the strategy of working with the residuals as a univariate batch should lead us to the potential outliers.

8

Outliers in Factorial Experiments

Factorial experiments play an important role as a tool for quality improvement. The conventional analyses of such experiments use least squares and summarize the results in an *analysis of variance (ANOVA) table*. Outliers can affect the mean squares and hence the F values in the ANOVA table. Typically the outlier or outliers have their greatest impact on the residual mean square, inflating its value. Then an F ratio that has this inflated mean square as its denominator may not indicate significance of the main effects or interactions that are being summarized in its numerator. For this reason alone, it is important to expose outliers in factorial experiments.

A complete factorial experiment involves k factors ($k \geq 2$), which we designate by A, B, ... , respectively. Each factor has a specified number of levels, with l_j levels for factor j ($j = 1, 2, \ldots, k$). The experiment then contains a total of $L = l_1 \times l_2 \times \cdots \times l_k$ cells. If each cell has m replications, the data consist of a total of $N = m \times l_1 \times l_2 \times \cdots \times l_k$ observations. Thus, in a $2 \times 3 \times 4$ experiment with 3 replications, factor A has two levels (frequently called high and low), factor B has three levels, and factor C has four levels, so that $L = (2)(3)(4) = 24$ cells and $N = (3)(2)(3)(4) = 72$ observations.

In an important class of designs each factor has the same number of levels. Then the complete k-factor experiment is called an l^k experiment. For example, a $3 \times 3 \times 3$ experiment is also called a 3^3 experiment in this shorthand notation.

8.1 Regression Methods for Identifying Outliers

Because both are based on least squares, analysis of factorial experiments has much in common with regression analysis. Indeed, although we seldom see the details in practice, it is possible to write a model for a factorial experiment as a multiple regression model. Thus, in practice, we could use some of the techniques described in Chapter 7 to identify outliers in factorial experiments.

Designed experiments, however, have two key features that set them apart from multiple regression when we consider diagnosis of outliers. First, many designs, including the complete factorial experiments, are balanced. Without giving a general definition of balance, we simply note that, among other consequences, it implies that all observations have the same leverage. If we wrote out the relations between observed and fitted values and calculated the diagonal elements of the hat matrix, we would find that they were all equal.

For example, if the experiment involved two factors and produced an $I \times J$ two-way layout with m observations per cell, the usual model in terms of main effects α_i and β_j and interactions $(\alpha\beta)_{ij}$ would be ($i = 1, \ldots, I$; $j = 1, \ldots, J$; $k = 1, \ldots, m$)

$$y_{ijk} = \mu + \alpha_i + \beta_j + (\alpha\beta)_{ij} + \epsilon_{ijk}.$$

The fitted value $\hat{y}_{ijk}$ would be the corresponding cell mean, $\bar{y}_{ij\cdot}$.

$$\hat{y}_{ijk} = \bar{y}_{ij\cdot} = \frac{1}{m}(y_{ij1} + y_{ij2} + \cdots + y_{ijm}).$$

We replace a subscript by a dot to indicate the result of averaging over that subscript. By inspecting the relation between $\hat{y}_{ijk}$ and y_{ijk} in this equation, we see that the diagonal element of the hat matrix is $1/m$. If m were only 1, the model would not include the interactions; instead we would have ($i = 1, \ldots, I$; $j = 1, \ldots, J$)

$$y_{ij} = \mu + \alpha_i + \beta_j + \epsilon_{ij}.$$

Now the fitted values would be

$$\hat{y}_{ij} = \bar{y}_{i\cdot} + \bar{y}_{\cdot j} - \bar{y}_{\cdot\cdot}$$

in which the combined coefficient of y_{ij} is

$$\frac{1}{J} + \frac{1}{I} - \frac{1}{IJ}.$$

That is, the diagonal element of the hat matrix is $(I+J-1)/IJ$. Both these examples have balanced leverage, as expected.

As the second key feature, the leave-out-one operation, which underlies the definition of the studentized residuals in Section 7.2, would be inconvenient in a balanced design because it would disrupt the balance.

Together, these two features suggest that studentized residuals would not offer much advantage in a factorial design and would not repay the effort required to calculate them. It may be worthwhile, however, to investigate the consequences of redefining $s^2(i)$ in a way that is compatible with factorial designs. The basic idea is simple: To obtain an s^2 for use with a particular observation, remove from the residual sum of squares all the terms associated with the cell in which the observation is located, and reduce the residual degrees of freedom accordingly (i.e., by $m - 1$ if each cell contains m replications).

The property of balance, which many designs enjoy, also provides a basis for robust analysis, because then a robust fit can reveal outliers as large residuals without having to contend with the adverse effects of points that have high leverage. Thus, we recommend using a robust analysis when the software is available.

Alternatively, one could replace the observations in each cell by their median and analyze the reduced set of data by the usual least-squares method. This straightforward exploratory step offers some protection against outliers when the number of observations per cell is at least three. To identify possible outliers, we return to the data within each cell, subtract the cell median from the rest of the observations in the cell, and then combine these residuals across all the cells (omitting the forced zero residual in each cell when m is odd) to form a single batch. When the within-cell variability is homogeneous, this form of pooling gives a more stable basis for identifying outliers.

Ullman (1989) uses a quality control technique called *analysis of ranges* to provide a simple tool for identifying outliers in replicated factorial experiments. Ullman's approach can be simplified when the number of cells is moderately large, say at least 12. Then one can compute the range of the observations within each cell and use this information to obtain a Shewhart R control chart. Out-of-control cells are then regarded as containing potential outliers. Because the R chart serves to identify outliers, it is more efficient to base the chart on a trimmed version of $\bar{R}$, called $\bar{R}(\alpha)$, which removes a specified number of the smallest and largest R's. Such trimmed control charts are discussed in Langenberg and Iglewicz (1986). Their control charts are a simple modification of the standard R chart, which has lower and upper control limits given by $D_3\bar{R}$ and $D_4\bar{R}$, respectively. The trimmed chart is obtained by replacing $\bar{R}$ with $k\bar{R}(\alpha)$ in computing the limits, where the constant k depends on the amount of trimming, the number of random observations used to compute the ranges, and the number of samples. The value of k has been observed to be close to 1 in all the cases studied. For example, $k = 1.039$ for 15% trimming (i.e., the smallest three and largest three ranges) in 20 samples of size 3.

8.2 Use of Modified R Charts for Identifying Outliers

The modified R charts identify outlying cells at a very conservative overall error rate when there are no outliers. For L cells, this error probability approximately equals $E = P(\text{at least one out-of-control range}) = 1 - (.9987)^L$. Assuming that the ranges are approximately normally distributed, the value .9987 is the probability that the range is below the 3σ upper control limit. More accurate results can be obtained using the exact distribution of the range based on a random normal sample. The approximate formula is used to obtain selected values of E as

L	E
12	.016
16	.021
20	.026
25	.032
30	.038
40	.051

This table shows that a trimmed-range control chart can be an effective conservative tool for identifying cells that may contain outliers. Although some professionals may prefer an exact significance level, the suggested procedure should be adequate for most purposes. Those desiring tests with specified significance levels can consult Ullman (1989) for details and references.

A slight modification of the standard R chart is required when the number of cells is relatively small. For such cases, Ullman (1989) tabulates values of H_L and H_U that give the lower and upper control limits as $H_L\bar{R}$ and $H_U\bar{R}$, respectively. For example, consider a 2^2 experiment with three replications per cell that has ranges 6.3, 3.7, 4.5, and 12.3. Then $\bar{R} = 6.7$. The appropriate values for comparisons at a 5% significance level are $H_L = 0.186$ and $H_U = 2.263$, respectively. Thus, the lower and upper decision limits are LDL = (0.186)(6.7) = 1.25 and UDL = (2.263)(6.7) = 15.16, implying that none of the four cells seem to contain outliers.

A word of caution is in order. Factorial experiments are designed in the hope that alternative choices of the factor levels will result in significant changes in the average response. Sometimes, however, the average response and the within-cell variability are related, so that cells with larger average responses tend to have larger variability and, consequently, higher expected ranges. Thus, out-of-control points can indicate either the presence of outliers or the absence of homogeneity of variance. As a consequence, all suspected outliers in factorial experiments need to be carefully analyzed. Box (1988) discusses the relationship between variability and response.

8.3 An Illustrative Example

One of the authors recently analyzed a 3^3 factorial experiment with two replications on grinding an alloy into powder. In this experiment, small values of the observed variable were considered good, but a number of auxiliary variables had to fall within specified limits. The resulting 27 ranges appear in Table 8.1. For a trimmed-mean R chart we trim the smallest 2 and the largest 2 ranges. Thus 0.1, 0.3, 16, and 21 are removed, and the average of the remaining 23 ranges is $\bar{R}(\alpha) = 3.765$. Langenberg and Iglewicz (1986) do not compute the constant multiple for samples of size 2, but from their other entries it seems reasonable to use $k = 1.05$. From *Glossary and Tables of Statistical Quality Control* (1983) we obtain $D_3 = 0$ and $D_4 = 3.267$, resulting in LCL = 0 and UCL = (1.05)(3.765)(3.267) = 12.92. This control chart is plotted in Figure 8.1. By comparison, the control limit for the R chart gives UCL = 15.01 instead of 12.92. Either limit identifies the two cells corresponding to the ranges 21 and 16 as out of control. Careful scrutiny of the data showed that these cells contained the observations from the first and third experimental runs, and these were larger than expected. Thus, some difficulty may have affected the gathering of the first few observations.

In order to assess the impact of these two outliers on the conclusions, we first obtained the ANOVA table for the original data. We then reanalyzed the data, replacing the two suspected values by their estimates from a least-squares regression model with interactions. The F ratios and P values from the two ANOVA tables are given in Table 8.2. The analysis of the original data indicates that the effects of factor A and all interactions are not significant, whereas the corresponding results for the modified data lead to significant main effects for A and significant BC and ABC interactions. In this instance, a significant ABC interaction proved to be unfortunate, as it caused difficulties with meeting the auxiliary constraints while, at the same time, trying to reduce y. In summary, this analysis illustrates the substantial impact that a few outliers can have on the conclusions of a factorial experiment analyzed by least squares.

Table 8.1

Ranges of data from a 3^3 factorial experiment on grinding an alloy into powder.

Cell	Levels	Range	Cell	Levels	Range	Cell	Levels	Range
1	000	2.5	10	100	21.0	19	200	0.1
2	001	5.0	11	101	10.3	20	201	1.4
3	002	4.0	12	102	0.6	21	202	1.4
4	010	0.7	13	110	1.6	22	210	1.5
5	011	7.4	14	111	1.9	23	211	0.9
6	012	2.7	15	112	0.9	24	212	2.8
7	020	9.2	16	120	0.3	25	220	6.1
8	021	8.3	17	121	4.4	26	221	16.0
9	022	2.0	18	122	7.5	27	222	3.5

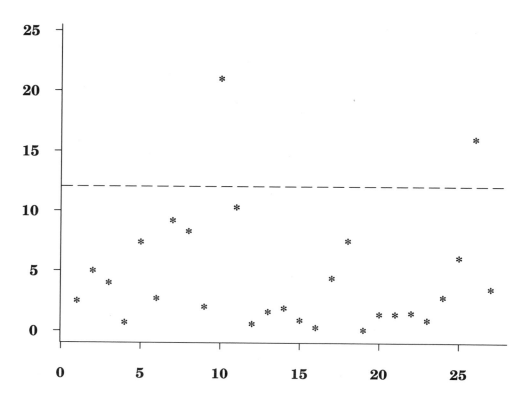

Figure 8.1. Modified R chart of ranges within the cells of a 3^3 factorial experiment (with 2 replications) on grinding an alloy into powder. (Table 8.1 gives the cell numbers.)

Table 8.2

F ratios and P values from the ANOVA tables for the original and modified data of the 3^3 factorial experiment.

	Original Data		Modified Data	
Source	F	P	F	P
A	2.65	.089	3.65	.039
B	5.61	.009	13.06	.000
C	6.66	.004	10.19	.001
AB	0.32	.865	0.82	.527
AC	0.73	.578	1.50	.231
BC	2.55	.062	2.95	.038
ABC	1.41	.235	2.51	.035

References

American Society for Quality Control, Statistics Division. 1983. *Glossary and Tables for Statistical Quality Control.* Milwaukee, WI: ASQC Quality Press. Tables used to obtain quality control chart limits for analyzing factorial experiments.

American Society for Testing and Materials. 1980. "Standard E-178, Standard Recommended Practice for Dealing with Outlying Observations." Philadelphia, PA: American Society for Testing and Materials. Discusses a number of classical methods for dealing with outliers in an industrial setting.

Andrews, D. F., P. J. Bickel, F. R. Hampel, P. J. Huber, W. H. Rogers, and J. W. Tukey. 1972. *Robust Estimates of Location: Survey and Advances.* Princeton, NJ: Princeton University Press. A pioneering, comprehensive study of robust estimators of location in symmetric distributions.

Atkinson, A. C. 1985. *Plots, Transformations and Regression: An Introduction to Graphical Methods of Diagnostic Regression Analysis.* New York: Oxford University Press. A fine treatment of transformations, plots, and diagnostics for varied regression models.

Barnett, V. 1978. "The Study of Outliers: Purpose and Model." *Applied Statistics* 27: 242–250. A very basic introduction to outliers.

Barnett, V., and T. Lewis. 1984. *Outliers in Statistical Data,* 2nd ed. New York: John Wiley & Sons. A well-written comprehensive text on outliers.

Beckman, R. J., and R. D. Cook. 1983. "Outlier..........s." *Technometrics* 25: 119–149. A worthwhile review article on outliers that is accompanied by informative discussion.

Belsley, D. A., E. Kuh, and R. E. Welsch. 1980. *Regression Diagnostics: Identifying Influential Data and Sources of Collinearity.* New York: John Wiley & Sons. A detailed and more advanced treatment of regression diagnostics.

Bendre, S. M., and B. K. Kale. 1985. "Masking Effect on Tests of Outliers in Exponential Samples." *Journal of the American Statistical Association* 80: 1020–1025. Compares the power of several tests for outliers from exponential distributions.

Box, G. E. P. 1988. "Signal-to-Noise Ratios, Performance Criteria, and Transformations." *Technometrics* 30: 1–17. A detailed discussion of the relationship between average response and variability in designed experiments.

Brant, R. 1990. "Comparing Classical and Resistant Outlier Rules." *Journal of the American Statistical Association* 85: 1083–1090. Power comparison of generalized ESD and boxplot rules for observations coming from the normal and selected non-normal populations.

Chatterjee, S., and A. S. Hadi. 1986. "Influential Observations, High Leverage Points, and Outliers in Linear Regression." *Statistical Science* 1: 379–416 (with discussion). A thorough review of practical aspects of regression diagnostics.

Collett, D., and T. Lewis. 1976. "The Subjective Nature of Outlier Rejection Procedures." *Applied Statistics* 25: 228–237. An interesting experiment on factors affecting visual identification of outliers.

Cook, R. D., and S. Weisberg. 1982. *Residuals and Influence in Regression.* New York: Chapman and Hall. A well-written book that covers many aspects of regression diagnostics.

D'Agostino, R. B., and G. L. Tietjen. 1971. "Simulation Probability Points of b_2 for Small Samples." *Biometrika* 58: 669–672. Tabulates the percentage points of b_2 that are used in this booklet.

Dixon, W. J. 1951. "Ratios Involving Extreme Values." *Annals of Mathematical Statistics* 22: 68–78. Gives percentage points of the Dixon tests.

Emerson, J. D., and D. C. Hoaglin. 1983. "Resistant Lines for y versus x," in D. C. Hoaglin, F. Mosteller, and J. W. Tukey, eds. *Understanding Robust and Exploratory Data Analysis.* New York: John Wiley & Sons. Gives a thorough discussion of the three-group resistant line method and briefly discusses other resistant regression approaches.

Emerson, J. D., and M. A. Stoto. 1983. "Transforming Data," in D. C. Hoaglin, F. Mosteller, and J. W. Tukey, eds. *Understanding Robust and Exploratory Data Analysis.* New York: John Wiley & Sons. Discusses use of letter values to transform data to a more symmetric set. Also gives a basic introduction to the practical aspects of data transformations.

Frigge, M., D. C. Hoaglin, and B. Iglewicz. 1989. "Some Implementations of the Boxplot." *The American Statistician* 43: 50–54. Describes varied options for constructing a boxplot and discusses their properties.

Gillespie, B. 1989. *Topics in Kaplan-Meier Estimation.* Ph.D. dissertation, Temple University, Philadelphia, PA. Gives detailed discussion of effect of data errors on the estimated survival distribution from censored data.

Gunter, B. 1988. "Subversive Data Analysis, Part II: More Graphics, Including My Favorite Example." *Quality Progress* 21: 77–78. The source of the gear-teeth data set.

Hampel, F. R. 1985. "The Breakdown Points of the Mean Combined with Some Rejection Rules." *Technometrics* 27: 95–107. Shows that a number of common outlier-detection procedures are susceptible to masking.

Hawkins, D. M. 1978. "Analysis of Three Tests for One or Two Outliers." *Statistica Neerlandica* 32: 137–148. Comparison of three older tests for two outliers from the normal distribution.

Hawkins, D. M. 1980. *Identification of Outliers.* New York: Chapman and Hall. A good and relatively short book on outliers; somewhat more mathematical than Barnett and Lewis (1984).

Hoaglin, D. C. 1983. "Letter Values: A Set of Selected Order Statistics," in D. C. Hoaglin, F. Mosteller, and J. W. Tukey, eds. *Understanding Robust and Exploratory Data Analysis.* New York: John Wiley & Sons. A careful discussion of letter values, their properties, and their uses.

Hoaglin, D.C. 1988. "Using Leverage and Influence to Introduce Regression Diagnostics." *College Mathematics Journal* 19: 387–401. An elementary treatment of leverage and regression diagnostics.

Hoaglin, D. C., and B. Iglewicz. 1987. "Fine-Tuning Some Resistant Rules for Outlier Labeling." *Journal of the American Statistical Association* 82: 1147–1149. Gives critical values for boxplot outlier identification rule.

Hoaglin, D. C., B. Iglewicz, and J. W. Tukey. 1986. "Performance of Some Resistant Rules for Outlier Labeling." *Journal of the American Statistical Association* 81: 991–999. Discusses small-sample probability properties of boxplot outlier-labeling rules.

Hoaglin, D. C., F. Mosteller, and J. W. Tukey, eds. 1983. *Understanding Robust and Exploratory Data Analysis.* New York: John Wiley & Sons. Discusses basic robust and exploratory methods and examines their connection with traditional statistical techniques and theory.

Hoaglin, D. C., and R. E. Welsch. 1978. "The Hat Matrix in Regression and ANOVA." *The American Statistician* 32: 17–22, 146. Introduces the hat matrix and discusses its use as a regression diagnostic tool.

Huber, P. J. 1981. *Robust Statistics.* New York: John Wiley & Sons. A theoretical text on robust statistics that contains the rule of thumb for deciding on high-leverage points in regression.

Iglewicz, B. 1983. "Robust Scale Estimators and Confidence Intervals for Location," in D. C. Hoaglin, F. Mosteller, and J. W. Tukey, eds. *Understanding Robust and Exploratory Data Analysis.* New York: John

Wiley & Sons. Provides the basic background needed to understand robust scale estimators and their properties.

Iglewicz, B., and D. C. Hoaglin. 1987. "Use of Boxplots for Process Evaluation." *Journal of Quality Technology* 19: 180–190. Uses a number of robust estimators in constructing combined Shewhart-type control charts.

Jain, R. B. 1981. "Percentage Points of Many-Outlier Detection Procedures." *Technometrics* 23: 71–76. Gives the percentage points of a generalized ESD procedure based on the kurtosis statistic.

Johnson, N. L., and S. Kotz. 1970. *Continuous Univariate Distributions–1.* Boston: Houghton Mifflin. One of a four-volume encyclopedic series that summarizes the basic properties of statistical distributions. Chapter 14 covers the lognormal distribution.

Kaplan, E. L., and P. Meier. 1958. "Nonparametric Estimation from Incomplete Observations." *Journal of the American Statistical Association* 53: 457–481. Introduces the Kaplan-Meier product-limit estimator, which is commonly used in obtaining a nonparametric estimate of the survival curve with censored data.

Kimber, A. C. 1982. "Tests for Many Outliers in an Exponential Sample." *Applied Statistics* 31: 263-271. Develops the test for multiple outliers from an exponential distribution that is used in this booklet.

Kimber, A. C. 1990. "Exploratory Data Analysis for Possibly Censored Data from Skewed Distributions." *Applied Statistics* 39: 21–30. Describes methods for computing boxplots from skewed and censored data.

Langenberg, P., and B. Iglewicz. 1986. "Trimmed Mean $\bar{X}$ and R Charts." *Journal of Quality Technology* 18: 152–161. Presents control charts based on trimmed means and ranges that are used in this booklet to identify outlying ANOVA cells in factorial experiments.

Morton, D. E., A. J. Saah, S. L. Silberg, W. L. Owens, M. A. Roberts, and M. D. Saah. 1982. "Lead Absorption in Children of Employees in a Lead-Related Industry." *American Journal of Epidemiology* 115: 549–555. Source for lead data used to illustrate the detection of outliers from a lognormal distribution.

Myers, R. H. 1990. *Classical and Modern Regression with Applications,* 2nd ed. Boston: PWS-Kent. An up-to-date intermediate text on regression.

Nelson, W. 1982. *Applied Life Data Analysis.* New York: John Wiley & Sons. A comprehensive book on industrial life data, with discussions of both the censored and uncensored cases.

Patel, K. R., G. S. Mudholkar, and I. J. L. Fernando. 1988. "Student's *t* Approximations for Three Simple Robust Estimators." *Journal of the American Statistical Association* 83: 1203–1210. Gives approximations for finding confidence intervals for the population mean based on trimmed means and Winsorized standard deviations.

Pearson, E. S., and H. O. Hartley, eds. 1966. *Biometrika Tables for Statisticians,* Vol. 1, 3rd. ed. London: Cambridge University Press. Includes percentage points of the kurtosis statistic.

Prescott, P. 1978. "Examination of Behaviour of Tests for Outliers When More Than One Outlier Is Present." *Applied Statistics* 27: 10–25. Comparison of tests for outliers from the normal distribution using sensitivity contours based on expected order statistics plus two outliers.

Rocke, D. M. 1992. "Estimation of Variation After Outlier Rejection." *Computational Statistics & Data Analysis* 13: 9–20. Shows that estimates of variance can be biased downward following use of a test procedure that identifies and then removes outliers.

Rosner, B. 1983. "Percentage Points for a Generalized ESD Many-Outlier Procedure." *Technometrics* 25: 165–172. Discusses the generalized ESD procedure and gives formula for obtaining percentage points.

Rousseeuw, P. J., and A. M. Leroy. 1987. *Robust Regression and Outlier Detection.* New York: John Wiley & Sons. An intermediate-level introduction to robust regression, including discussion of computer programs and basic methodology.

Shapiro, S. S. 1986. *How to Test Normality and Other Distributional Assumptions.* [The ASQC Basic References in Quality Control: Statistical Techniques, Vol. 3] Milwaukee, WI: American Society for Quality Control. Gives introduction to tests for distributional assumptions.

Shapiro, S. S., and M. B. Wilk. 1965. "An Analysis of Variance Test for Normality (complete samples)." *Biometrika* 52: 591–611. Introduces the Shapiro-Wilk test for normality and also for the detection of outliers.

Shiffler, R. E. 1988. "Maximum *Z* Scores and Outliers." *The American Statistician* 42: 79–80. Finds the upper bound on standard Z-scores.

Shumway, R. H., A. S. Azari, and P. Johnson. 1989. "Estimating Mean Concentrations Under Transformation for Environmental Data with Detection Limits." *Technometrics* 31: 347–356. Discusses the need for transformations in environmental data.

Siegel, A. F. 1982. "Robust Regression Using Repeated Medians." *Biometrika* 69: 242–244. The first technical discussion of the repeated-median approach to robust regression.

Tietjen, G. L., and R. H. Moore. 1972. "Some Grubbs-Type Statistics for the Detection of Several Outliers." *Technometrics* 14: 583–597. Development of the Tietjen and Moore test for identifying a group of r outliers.

Tukey, J. W. 1977. *Exploratory Data Analysis.* Reading, MA: Addison-Wesley. A basic introduction to exploratory data analysis written by its founder. This book played a key role in introducing the topic to the statistical profession.

Ullman, N. R. 1989. "The Analysis of Means (ANOM) for Signal and Noise." *Journal of Quality Technology* 21: 111–127. Discusses use of the analysis-of-range procedure for detecting outlying cells in designed experiments.

Appendix

Table A.1

1% and 5% two-sided critical values for Rosner's generalized ESD many-outlier procedure.

n	$\alpha = .05$					$\alpha = .01$				
	λ_1	λ_2	λ_3	λ_4	λ_5	λ_1	λ_2	λ_3	λ_4	λ_5
10	2.29	2.22	2.13			2.48	2.39	2.27		
11	2.35	2.29	2.22			2.56	2.48	2.39		
12	2.41	2.35	2.29			2.64	2.56	2.48		
13	2.46	2.41	2.35			2.70	2.64	2.56		
14	2.51	2.46	2.41			2.76	2.70	2.64		
15	2.55	2.51	2.46			2.81	2.76	2.70		
16	2.59	2.55	2.51			2.85	2.81	2.76		
17	2.62	2.59	2.55			2.89	2.85	2.81		
18	2.65	2.62	2.59			2.93	2.89	2.85		
19	2.68	2.65	2.62			2.97	2.93	2.89		
20	2.71	2.68	2.65	2.62	2.59	3.00	2.97	2.93	2.89	2.85
25	2.82	2.80	2.78	2.76	2.73	3.14	3.11	3.09	3.06	3.03
30	2.91	2.89	2.88	2.86	2.84	3.24	3.22	3.20	3.18	3.16
35	2.98	2.97	2.95	2.94	2.92	3.32	3.30	3.29	3.27	3.25
40	3.04	3.03	3.01	3.00	2.99	3.38	3.37	3.36	3.34	3.33
45	3.09	3.08	3.07	3.06	3.05	3.44	3.43	3.41	3.40	3.39
50	3.13	3.12	3.11	3.10	3.09	3.48	3.47	3.46	3.46	3.45
60	3.20	3.19	3.19	3.18	3.17	3.56	3.55	3.55	3.54	3.53
70	3.26	3.25	3.25	3.24	3.24	3.62	3.62	3.61	3.60	3.60
80	3.31	3.30	3.30	3.29	3.29	3.67	3.67	3.66	3.66	3.65
90	3.35	3.34	3.34	3.34	3.33	3.72	3.71	3.71	3.70	3.70
100	3.38	3.38	3.38	3.37	3.37	3.75	3.75	3.75	3.74	3.74

Table A.2

Approximate 10%, 5%, and 1% critical values of b_2, the sample kurtosis, in samples from a normal distribution.

n	0.10	0.05	0.01
7	3.20	3.55	4.23
8	3.31	3.70	4.53
9	3.43	3.86	4.82
10	3.53	3.95	5.00
12	3.55	4.05	5.20
15	3.62	4.13	5.30
20	3.68	4.17	5.36
25	3.68	4.16	5.30
30	3.68	4.11	5.21
35	3.68	4.10	5.13
40	3.67	4.06	5.04
45	3.65	4.00	4.94
50	3.62	3.99	4.88

Source: D'Agostino, R. B., and G. L. Tietjen. 1971. "Simulation Probability Points of b_2 for Small Samples." *Biometrika* 58: 669–672. Entries from Table 1 on p. 670.

Table A.3

1% and 5% critical values for three versions of Dixon tests.

n	λ_{11} 1%	λ_{11} 5%	λ_{21} 1%	λ_{21} 5%	λ'_{10} 1%	λ'_{10} 5%
4	.991	.955			.922	.831
5	.916	.807	.995	.976	.831	.717
6	.805	.689	.951	.872	.737	.621
7	.740	.610	.885	.780	.694	.570
8	.683	.554	.829	.710	.638	.524
9	.635	.512	.776	.657	.594	.492
10	.597	.477	.726	.612	.564	.464
11	.566	.450	.679	.576		
12	.541	.428	.642	.546	.520	.429
13	.520	.410	.615	.521		
14	.502	.395	.593	.501	.485	.397
15	.486	.381	.574	.483		
16	.472	.369	.557	.467	.461	.376
17	.460	.359	.542	.453		
18	.449	.349	.529	.440	.438	.354
19	.439	.341	.517	.428		
20	.430	.334	.506	.419	.417	.340
21	.421	.327	.496	.410		
22	.414	.320	.487	.402		
23	.407	.314	.479	.395		
24	.400	.309	.471	.388		
25	.394	.304	.464	.382	.386	.316
26	.389	.299	.457	.376		
27	.383	.295	.450	.370		
28	.378	.291	.444	.365		
29	.374	.287	.438	.360		
30	.369	.283	.433	.355	.368	.300

Sources: Entries for λ_{11} are from Dixon (1951), Table II on p. 74. The λ_{21} values are from Dixon (1951), Table V on p. 77. The λ'_{10} entries are from Barnett and Lewis (1984), Table XIVb on p. 390.

Table A.4

Values of k for boxplot rule with specified probability of at least one outside observation per random normal sample.

n	0.05	0.10
5	5.6	3.7
6	2.9	2.0
7	3.0	2.3
8	2.2	1.8
9	3.3	2.7
10	2.4	2.0
11	2.7	2.2
12	2.2	1.8
13	2.8	2.3
14	2.5	2.0
15	2.5	2.1
16	2.3	1.9
17	2.6	2.2
18	2.4	2.0
19	2.6	2.2
20	2.2	1.9
30	2.2	2.0
40	2.2	2.0
50	2.2	2.0
75	2.3	2.1
100	2.2	2.1
200	2.4	2.2
300	2.4	2.2

Source: Hoaglin, D. C., and B. Iglewicz. 1987. "Fine-Tuning Some Resistant Rules for Outlier Labeling." *Journal of the American Statistical Association* 82: 1147–1149. Entries from Table 1 on p. 1149. Reprinted by permission of the American Statistical Association.

Table A.5

5% critical values for Kimber's test for finding up to r upper outliers from an exponential distribution.

n	$r = 2$		$r = 3$		
	s_2	s_1	s_3	s_2	s_1
10	.434	.483			
11	.401	.453			
12	.372	.427			
13	.348	.403			
14	.327	.383			
15	.308	.364	.306	.321	.380
16	.292	.347	.287	.304	.363
17	.277	.332	.271	.288	.347
18	.264	.318	.257	.274	.333
19	.252	.306	.248	.266	.325
20	.241	.294	.236	.255	.313
22	.222	.273	.216	.235	.291
24	.206	.256	.196	.214	.269
26	.193	.240	.183	.200	.251
28	.181	.227	.170	.188	.236
30	.171	.215	.163	.180	.229
35	.150	.190	.139	.155	.198
40	.134	.171	.125	.140	.179
45	.121	.155	.113	.128	.166
50	.111	.142	.101	.114	.147
60	.095	.122	.086	.097	.127
70	.083	.107	.075	.085	.111
80	.074	.096	.069	.078	.103
90	.067	.087	.062	.071	.093
100	.061	.079	.056	.064	.085
120	.052	.068	.047	.053	.070
140	.046	.060	.042	.048	.063

Source: Kimber, A. C. 1982. "Tests for Many Outliers in an Exponential Sample." *Applied Statistics* 31: 263–271. Entries from Tables 1 and 2 on p. 266. Reprinted by permission of the Royal Statistical Society.

Index